24th April '10.

To Liz,

Thank you for your support.

Best wishes,

Tom.

BUILDING BRIDGES

A history of the Foyle Hospice

Dr Keith Munro

FOYLE HOSPICE PUBLISHING

Published in December 2005 by

Foyle Hospice Publishing
Foyle Hospice
61 Culmore Road
BT48 8JE
T: (028) 7135 9888

Printed by
RCD Print Ltd
The Resource Centre
Racecourse Road
Derry BT48 8BA

ISBN 0 9551840 0 2

Dedicated to the people of the north-west corner of Ireland who have, in myriad ways, contributed to the success of Foyle Hospice; to Dr Tom McGinley without whom it could not exist, and to Deirdre, his beloved wife, whose wholehearted support allowed him the time and the space to fulfil his dream.

Acknowledgements

This book is the fulfilment of a promise made to Tom McGinley before I retired from General Practice on 29th September, 2003.

I wanted to create a book for all those who have taken part in the building up and running of Foyle Hospice, as well as for the public, who have given so generously of their time and money over the years.

The story of 'how it all happened' was one which needed to be told. I felt that this book about Foyle Hospice should be both a written and a pictorial history. It should be beautiful in its presentation and truly be a celebration of the wonderful facility we now have. To that end I am indebted to *R.C.D. Printers Ltd.*, who have been very patient with my specific thoughts and ideas for layout.

In giving thanks to all who assisted in this project, it is difficult to know where to start. Many names have been mentioned in the text of the book and more are featured in photographs. Hundreds of others have been so supportive in many ways, and I must apologise if anyone's name has been left out. It is just not possible to include everyone. I find Deirdre McGinley's recorded words written in her biography of Tom very apt:

> "I hope that the community as a whole know how much their efforts at fundraising are so much appreciated, however small they think their input is. Nothing is too small – it is all cumulative. I find it impossible to mention all the people and groups who have made Tom's dream possible and I hope I am forgiven for that, but heartfelt thanks goes out to all of them. I have never seen a project develop with such momentum in all my life, and on and on it goes." (2002)

Some, however, must be thanked specifically.

All local newspapers, including the *Londonderry Sentinel, Belfast Telegraph* and the *Derry News*, have been so very generous in their willingness to allow photographs to be used as well as text. They have given their total support for Foyle Hospice since the concept was launched in the 1980s.

My deepest thanks to the *Derry Journal*, especially, for permission to reproduce many, many photos.

To *R.C.D. Printers Ltd.* for their immediate willingness to take on the publishing and printing of this book.

BBC Radio Foyle needs very special thanks, not only for the many interviews concerning the hospice over more than twenty years, but for the 'live' and very memorable broadcast of the Opening Day in June 1991.

To Sean Doherty, of *Highland Radio,* who never missed an opportunity to promote the work of the hospice.

To *Veritas Publishers* (Dublin) for their permission to reproduce short passages from Bishop Daly's book.

To various members of the administrative staff at the hospice for my constant niggling about facts or photos; also to the many people I interviewed who were so willing to share their heartfelt memories.

A big thank you must go to Garbhán Downey, whose willingness to proofread the chapters was immediate, sincere and wholehearted. The pernickety nature of the work needs special talents. He has them.

Last, and by no means least, my deepest and most profound thanks to Tom, himself. To have had the opportunity to stand beside a man of Tom's stature for more than twenty years, as he battled day and night with the thousand-and-one problems of founding and running the hospice, has been a great privilege and, at times, awe-inspiring.

More recently we sat together night after night and struggled over facts, sequences and photos. It has been a joy, if exhausting, for us both. Each time we got it right, some new fact was located or recollected and had to be included! Then another photograph was found that absolutely had to go into the book.

The facts and photos that combine to make up this book have been researched over a period of almost two years. Tom has been the potter who moulded this 'clay' together.

Thanks, Tom, for everything.

Keith Munro
October 2005

Contents

Foyle Hospice Philosophy

Hospice care is based on a philosophy which recognises the need to treat each person with dignity, respect and compassion, irrespective of their cultural or religious background. Services include inpatient care, homecare, daycare, bereavement support and 24 hour telephone advice.

The hospice is committed to:

- Providing the best possible quality of life for our patients, with special emphasis on expert pain relief and symptom control.

- Combining excellent nursing and medical care with holistic support that recognises practical, emotional, social and spiritual needs.

- Maintaining support systems to help patients live as actively as possible until death.

- Respecting the patient's autonomy and choice, such as place of care and the various treatment options.

- Supporting the family and those who matter to the patient during the illness and in bereavement.

- Sharing truthful information about diagnosis, treatment and prognosis with patients, in an attentive and non-intrusive way.

- Cooperating and collaborating with other professionals and support agencies, in particular, primary health care teams and hospitals.

- Disseminating knowledge by providing ongoing, multi-professional, educational training programmes.

- Recognising and valuing the contribution of all volunteers.

All hospice services are free of charge to patients and their families.

Chapter One

"We need a hospice and need it now!"

The Valley of Search

The steed of this Valley is patience; without patience the wayfarer on this journey will reach nowhere and attain no goal. Nor should he ever be downhearted.

(Bahá'í writings)

During the summer of 1983, Dr Tom McGinley was in the middle of coaching ladies for the Foyle Female Five organised by the local Sparta athletic club. This was the first ever local ladies-only run. Just before going out to training one evening, he read an article in the *Belfast Telegraph*.* Money was being raised for the Northern Ireland Hospice by organising a 'walk in Derry' in September of that year. Lynn Riddel, a well-known journalist at the time, was to take part. Suddenly, he realised that if fund-raising for Foyle Hospice did not start immediately, money raised in Derry would be channelled to Belfast and would slow down the building of a hospice for the North-West. What annoyed him more was that sponsorship forms for the Northern Ireland Hospice fundraising event were available in the very sports complex where they were training! Tom's steely determination speedily kicked in.

Of course, the rest of Northern Ireland would need a hospice, perhaps eventually more than one. However, one thing was certain, families in the North-West could not be expected to travel all the way to Belfast to receive specialist palliative care. "We need a hospice in this area and we need it now," stated Tom. "Fundraising, in a big way, is imperative."

That night at training he announced to the assembled ladies, "We need to block the money being raised for a hospice outside our area." Those present came from Tyrone, Derry and Donegal and he asked if they would fundraise in their respective areas. He emphasized that this hospice would serve the whole of

* See Picture Gallery at the back of the book.

the north-west of Ireland. This was the beginning of serious fundraising. About 1300 females took part on Saturday 1st October, 1983, and sponsorship for the hospice raised some £10,000, no mean sum in those years.

Little was it thought, in the euphoria of launching the campaign, that more than a million pounds would eventually be required. Levels of faith and enthusiasm were high.

The inaugural female mini-marathon in 1983

Significant amongst those who attended that historic training session were staff members of Aberfoyle Surgery, Dr Tom's own practice. They had called themselves 'McGinley's Angels'. They became the pioneers of fundraising for the hospice.

Jean Begley said, "I threatened to buy him a tin of Brasso as I constantly told him he had a brass neck. He didn't mind who or how he asked for donations. If a drug rep wanted to see him he would take me aside and insist I ask them to make a donation to the hospice. If they declined then they got short shrift! I remember well the day Dr McGinley decided to launch the Weekly Draw on the radio. 'Jean,' he said, 'Radio Foyle is going to announce the draw on Don O'Doherty's afternoon show. The surgery telephone number will be given out for those wishing to join the draw. You can man the hotline and take details.' That's exactly how I spent my afternoon. It was indeed a 'hot' line. The response was amazing. Needless to say I became one of the first promoters – not that I had any choice! The draw became very successful. I'm still a promoter after 20 years. I never did buy him the tin of Brasso but he achieved his goal as only he could have done."

His next move was to announce the plans for a hospice to the local media. Two other firsts occurred during that exciting period. The first sponsored walk was launched for the hospice. This went from Tillie and Henderson's factory on

McGinley's Angels, pioneers of fundraising, (from left) Pauline, Ann Marie, Sharon, Dr Tom, Jean and Annette. Sadly Ann Marie died in England. Jean Begley became Dr Tom's first voluntary hospice secretary.

Abercorn Road to Bridgend and back. Tom comments, "I wanted to make sure they passed Pennyburn Chapel when Mass-goers were coming out so they had a better opportunity to raise extra funds."

Around that time the first cheque presentation appeared in the press. A group from Marlborough Road had been raising money for a hospital on the west bank. When they realised it was not going to happen, they handed the balance of their funds to the Foyle Hospice Fundraising Campaign. The first Support Group was set up during January 1984 by Don and Celine Carlin from William Street in Derry. Others groups followed at Top of the Hill, Carnhill and Iniscarn Crescent in the Creggan.

In the autumn of 1983 another GP, Dr Keith Munro, (author), had been visiting a terminally ill patient together with a medical student. Aware of the difficulties he saw, and the lack of facilities for the patient, he commented to the student that what the city really needed was a hospice. He mentioned this to Dr Ailbe Bierne, a Geriatric Consultant at Altnagelvin Hospital, and was told that if he wished to build a hospice he had better go and see Tom McGinley who had started a campaign. Tom suggested forming a small steering committee. Together

One of the first large cheques towards the Appeal Fund. Helen McGuire, organiser of a Wine & Cheese Party in the Prehen Boathouse is presenting a cheque for £1,500 to Dr McGinley. Other ladies involved were (front from left) Betty Villa, Ann McGonagle, Margaret Curley, Marion Kee, Anne Speer and Bernie McLaughlin. (Back from left) Ann Colhoun, Aileen McCleery, Anna Sweeney (deceased), Kathleen Connolly and Ruth Morrow. (March 1984)

with Grainne Nugent, Tom's sister-in-law, and Hugh McAlliney, a local bank manager, the first administrative structure of Foyle Hospice was set up.

Ken Goodall, a teacher and well-known rugby player, was invited to join the steering committee and then, by January 1984, it was decided to have an official launch for a hospice appeal. The goal would be to raise £500,000 for the future Inpatient Unit. The launch took place in the Guildhall.

The new Foyle Bridge was to be the symbol of the Hospice.

During February 1984, Dr Tom and Dr Keith were invited to lunch by the Western Health and Social Services Board. The Board made it clear that no financial assistance would be available. Indeed it was felt by some members of the Board that Dr McGinley had taken on too much. This was like a red rag to a McGinley bull! His determination and vision were strong. Such negative opinions were not going to stop the big push.

During March, the first Car Draw was held in the Everglades Hotel and the following month the first Flag Day organised. Also in April, Donal Dunn and Willie Doherty ran from Dublin to Derry and raised £1000 (see Picture Gallery). At Easter, Margaret McLaughlin and Helena Byrne, who both worked as Health Visitors in Aberfoyle Surgery, took on the organisation of a five-mile sponsored walk.

Dr McGinley receives one of the first cheques (in March 1984) for the Foyle Hospice Appeal from the Prehen Boathouse Keep-fit Group. (From left) Maureen Gallagher, Margaret Molloy, Betty Kane, Dr Tom, Pamela Donaghy, Kieran McGrory (supervisor of the Prehen Boathouse). Betty Kane died in the Inpatient Unit in 2004. (See Picture Gallery)

Mayor Len Green receives the Foyle Hospice Steering Committee for the launch of the Hospice Appeal. (From left) Ken Goodall, Dr Tom McGinley, Gráinne Nugent, and Dr Keith Munro. Bishop Daly and Bishop Mehaffey are standing behind with Hugh McAlliney. (January 1984)

Margaret recollects that time:

"My first involvement with the hospice was in Aberfoyle Surgery where I worked as a Health Visitor for 18 years along with Helena Byrne. I witnessed the early years of the hospice movement in the North-West. Dr McGinley spoke a lot about his plans for a hospice. Like other members of staff, I felt he had taken on a mammoth challenge and deserved a lot of support. Funds had to be raised. Dr Tom, along with Helena and me, started up a well-baby clinic and a pre-school medical clinic. All the mothers were 'pressurised' to train for these runs and walks. Like some other people, I wasn't a runner, so a sponsored walk was suggested by Dr Tom and I took it on to organise it. The first walk - a distance of five miles – was in 1984. It was a great success. The Mayor, Len Green, started it off at the Guildhall. We walked to Newbuildings and back to Riverview House where all walkers had refreshments. My colleagues, friends and local shops donated food. We raised £9000. Colleagues in Strabane, Limavady and Castlederg also took part. One of the people I was introduced to then was the late Joe McElroy (Strabane). He did a lot of fundraising

Margaret McLaughlin (health visitor) who, with colleagues, organised the first sponsored walk at Easter, 1984. To her left is Helena Byrne.

and became very involved. His family and friends still continue the good work. Sadly, my dear friend, Helena, who helped me so much, later died in the hospice in June 1999.

"The sponsored walk continued annually for many years but not on the same route. When the headquarters was purchased at 9 Crawford Square we used it as a starting point. One year we did the two bridges and afterwards we had a band to brighten up the atmosphere. We had some enjoyable days on the walks, and local stores gave us a lot of support."

Margaret eventually retired from work in 1989, but felt she would like to continue, in some small way, caring for people so she decided to become a volunteer at the hospice. This gives her great satisfaction and happiness.

Margaret still serving in the hospice.

Ever since his recovery from serious illness in the 1960s, running had been his passion, so Dr Tom began organising the first Foyle Hospice Female Run for June 1984. He wanted to promote this big effort as much as he could. He knew that the Dublin Female Mini-Marathon was being run shortly, so he and Gerry Craig, who worked at the Templemore Sports Complex, set off for Dublin to see what they could do to drum up massive support. Thousands of ladies were registering at the RDS complex in Dublin and both men were determined to display posters there about the Female Run back home in Derry. These posters were inviting ladies to come to Derry, promising free accommodation and free transport. They needed to gain access to the central position within the RDS to maximize the effect of their display. They drove up, with a certain amount of bravado. They were refused entry and turned away. No vehicles were allowed in except strictly by prior arrangement. Once outside again Tom had a brilliant idea. Why not put up the 'Urgent: Doctor on Call' sign on the dashboard and try to gain access by a different route? So he placed it on the dashboard. As a result the car was escorted immediately to the very position they wanted! Gerry and Tom displayed their welcoming posters and, as a result, several hundred ladies came to Derry that June from many counties throughout Ireland. None of them had to pay anything for their accommodation, which was enthusiastically offered by local supporters of the new hospice movement. Many stayed in the Bogside which had been so prominent during the 'Troubles'. The whole climate had now changed, however. Even a gig was organised for them at the local rugby club. These ladies raised large sums in sponsorship and many came back in subsequent years. The run was a huge success and more than 1000 ladies completed the course. The big push had started.

A Listening Ear
Brendan Duddy recollects the early years

Marathon running was a fever in 1981-82. Tom got caught up in it as well and he joined Bernie Mount and myself on our training runs. Running 70-80 miles weekly on the roads was not unusual especially when a marathon approached. Tom had already decided in his own mind that a hospice would be necessary for the North-West. He was also aware that a group in Belfast were planning to build a hospice and that their plan was to start fundraising in Derry. He was determined that any money raised for the hospice would stay in our own area.

Very quickly it dawned on me that Tom was using these long runs in training as a means of bouncing off me his endless stream of ideas about the pros and cons of such a major venture. On the first training run, the hospice concept was totally and fully in place in Tom's mind. Not only that, he had already decided that the optimum site would be at Boomhall. The fact that this land belonged to the Orange Order did not in any way worry him. In those days there was terrible political turmoil in the country. They were the days of hunger strikes and it was a time of almost no hope. I wanted to talk politics and the future of the country but Tom's passion was the pain suffered by cancer patients and the total inadequacy of dealing with it. I had no choice but to become his 'listening ear'. One should remember that in those days the word 'cancer' was rarely spoken of and terms such as 'the big C' were used. There was a mindset of 'cancer equals pain equals death'. On many visits to hospices in London, he had seen that patients could die with dignity and free from pain. Many professionals were scared to use morphine in adequate doses because of the fear of addiction, and the phrase "keep the strong stuff until the end" was commonly heard. Some years later, after a TV programme on RTE, in which Tom took part, called 'Cries for Help – The Hospices', he showed me a letter he received from a lady in Cork. The programme was presented by Patricia Coyle, a girl from Derry. In the letter the lady spoke of her nephew who had died a few years earlier from cancer. She had sent for her local doctor to get some relief for the severe pain he was suffering. The doctor said that it was unwise to give him an injection of morphine because, in his words, "We will need it for the end." Her nephew died later that night in agony without the benefit of any pain relief. Understandably she had remained very angry since.

Communicating the truth with dying patients was always a problem at that time. The conspiracy of silence was in common use. This meant that when a doctor called to see a patient, who was terminally ill, he would be met at the door by the wife or husband and instructed not to tell the patient about the poor prognosis. Similarly the patient would request that the rest of the family should not be told. This created major problems.

The new Foyle Bridge was due to be opened in the summer of 1984. The symbolism of this bridge was central to Tom's thinking about a hospice building. The bridge as a symbol of life's journey appealed to him. He was of the opinion that some people with a terminal illness, passing over the bridge from this life to the next, would require specialised care. Ideally this care should be provided at home but in some cases it was going to require a specialist inpatient unit. He also felt that differences and divisions between the west bank and the east bank of the river could be bridged anew to meet the needs of people and communities. It would also signify a bridge across the border into Donegal. He realised that a homecare service would first have to be established and when this was firmly in place an Inpatient Unit would follow.

The death of his mother, in the family home in Donegal, in February 1986, brought Tom to a complete halt. His enthusiasm disappeared completely. He started making all sorts of excuses for not proceeding further with plans for a building. Arguments such as 'enough money would not be available' and 'the ongoing costs could not be met by the public' were presented. He felt the home-care service, which was up-and-running, would be adequate.

He often recalled how, following his serious illness in 1966/67, his mother used to accompany him daily for a walk on the Buncrana Road as he tried to regain his strength. Each day she encouraged him to do that 'wee bit extra'. He attributed his complete recovery to her dedication to prayer.

Tom was determined that prejudices resulting from politics or religion would play no part in the hospice. One incident particularly hurt him which involved members of a local Presbyterian church. They invited the Chairman of the Northern Ireland Hospice to talk about the Hospice Movement in general. This person was later to write to Dr Munro, who was neither a Catholic nor a nation-alist, explaining how that church group felt that our Foyle Hospice had too much nationalist input! This group subsequently, became very supportive of the whole project. Around the same time, I was in Tom's sitting room one evening when a Catholic priest, a very dedicated man in many ways, and who has since died, called to see Tom. He indicated that he felt there should be a strong Catholic influence with regard to the local hospice and was indeed inviting him-self onto the hospice committee. The tension of the conversation became almost unbearable. Tom was absolutely resolute regards the hospice ethos. It would be Christian and neutral, with each denomination having equal right and space for members of their flock.

Mayor Len Green fires the gun to start the first Foyle Hospice Female Five (June1984)

18

Sister Anna leads the group! (June 1984)

This is the way it has remained and those moments of tension, which could have destroyed the entire hospice concept of dignity and equality in treatment and in death, were stopped in their tracks with full frontal honesty and openness.

All the churches now work in beautiful harmony in the Foyle Hospice. This seems so normal and natural now, that it is easy to forget the courage and foresight of Tom in the mid-1980s.

This sudden challenge, "We need a hospice and we need it now!" laid down by Dr Tom McGinley, had not come out of a clear blue sky. Tom had been acutely aware, for a long time, of the shortcomings in services for those with a terminal illness. He had joined the Aberfoyle Medical Practice in the early 1960s where he, with the late Dr Peter Fallon and Dr Vincent Cavanagh, worked together as a medical triumvirate. Peter was the most senior of them and was the one who imparted his expert knowledge of how to provide care for terminally ill patients in their own homes. Tom's interest in that field was sparked off by their intensive work caring for a young lad who was doing his A level examinations. His partner Dr Vincent Cavanagh takes up the story:

> "The patient required frequent morphine injections for the severe pain he was experiencing from a malignant tumour in his knee. These

injections were given as near to four hourly as we could, but the demands of practice sometimes prevented us from arriving at this home in De Burgh Square (in the Rosemount area) exactly on time.

"One must remember that in those days to give morphine injections outside the four-hour limit was regarded as highly dangerous. Tom was particularly upset one night when this particular lad asked the dreaded question, 'Doctor, am I not going to get better?' This was the first time Tom had ever been asked this question.

"In those days, to tell a patient about their poor prognosis was regarded as unethical and so Tom lied to him. His medical education up till then as a student, and his few years after qualifying in hospital had not prepared him for this.

Michael Donaghy, who was the inspiration for Dr Tom learning how to help those who were terminally ill.

"The total emphasis at the time was on 'cure'. Patients with a poor prognosis were not given much priority. Tom became fascinated with, and engrossed in, the concept in the concept of terminal care. He was to take time out to study for higher examinations in anaesthetics and succeeded in obtaining a specialist degree. To acquire this degree is a major achievement in itself. To get it while working full time in general practice is almost unheard of and, as far as we know, is unique. Tom subsequently put his anaesthetic experience to good use and many procedures were carried out in the patients' own homes. This included things like epidurals, intrathecal phenol, inter-costal blocks and other nerve blocks. He regularly spent his holidays attending hospices in England, especially St Joseph's in Hackney. While there, he had the privilege of meeting Dame Cicely Saunders on a few occasions. She used to visit on a fairly regular basis. He learned a great deal from skilled people who worked in practice and not just in theory.

By the late 1970s, Tom talked of his plans about starting a hospice for the North-West. This was a terrible time in terms of civil disturbance, shooting, bombing and violence of all kinds. Many deaths occurred and very many more injuries. Fundraising for such a project would have been extremely difficult if not impossible. However, by the early 1980s, that climate had changed and there was an air of optimism in the area. In 1983, he commenced fundraising, with all our secretarial staff heavily involved."

Now, with his specialist degree, Tom soon got invitations and became a regular speaker locally as well as in Belfast and Craigavon. News travelled fast and he was invited to speak to various groups of doctors throughout the Republic of Ireland. He became involved, in an advisory capacity, with Marie Curie Nurses. Gretta Linehan, who nursed for Marie Curie, recalls, "Dr McGinley called every night to see his patients who were dying of cancer even when he was off duty." During that time Tom was also invited to give advice on pain relief and symptom control at both Altnagelvin Hospital as well as St Columb's Hospital.

Seeds were being sown.

Chapter Two

Supporting Pillars – Memories of Hospice Support Groups

During 1984, representatives of many support groups that sprang up to help financially in the founding of Foyle Hospice met with Dr McGinley in the Everglades Hotel to plan the way forward. They came from William Street, Prehen, Iniscarn Crescent, Top of the Hill and Carnhill. Other groups were formed over the subsequent three years. Recorded here are memories of the main groups who were essential as supporting pillars for the fundraising campaign.

Number One – William Street Support Group
Founded 15th January, 1984

The first of the hospice support groups began in William Street in Derry. Sadly, for Celine and Don Carlin, it came about as a result of the untimely death of their four-year-old daughter, Eileen. She had been diagnosed with a brain

*Dr McGinley with officers of the first support group set up in William Street.
(From right) Pat McCallion, Celine Carlin, Dr Tom, Mary Kelly (treasurer)*

tumour and died in the Royal Victoria Hospital for Sick Children on 8th December, 1983. She had been sent for a scan to Belfast and, when the shock diagnosis was made, she was operated on immediately. Unfortunately it was too late. They both sat with her for three days before she slipped away and was brought home to be laid to rest. Their memories of that sad time are as fresh today as they were more than twenty years ago.

"When Eileen was only three, and before she became sick, Dr McGinley used to visit our house on nights when he was on-call for the practice. He used to speak about the formation of a hospice," said Celine.

The family were patients of Aberfoyle Practice. They listened with great interest but it was only after the severe grief of Eileen's death that the idea of beginning a support group was kick-started. The idea of raising money for others dying from cancer became a passion. Apart from themselves they gathered together a loyal and active group of ladies. Their first meeting was held on 16th January 1984. Soon they ran their first Guest Tea in Pilot's Row and raised about £500. Don recollects that subsequent events were so popular that they ran short of

*Eileen Carlin (4yrs)
Died 8th December,1983*

Don and Celine Carlin, founders of the William Street Hospice Support Group.

tables. Then there were dances in the Parish Hall. They managed to run one a month. Indeed one of the most important draws, for two cars, took place during Hospice Week, at a special dance held in St Eugene's Parish Hall on Saturday 22nd June, 1991.

"After about fifteen years," said Celine, "we eventually had to fold up because of Don's health. At the end we handed over £2,500 but must have raised many thousands over that period. We also helped form a group in Trench Road as well as in Carnhill. Alistair Kinkaid and Joan Brown were very helpful contacts, who worked at the fundraising centre in Crawford Square.

"At one time I had 225 members in the Weekly Draw! It was amazing! The money was always brought to the house. I never had to chase it up. Then, even though the group had folded, we had a commemorative supper on the tenth anniversary of the hospice. This was to thank every one for their support in the Parish Hall where most of the events were held."

The Prehen Support Group
Founded in early 1984

"Margaret was a district nurse involved in Great James Street Practice," said Gerry Patton. "This was in early 1984. She was friendly with Angela McIntyre and Tom McGinley. They both came out to Prehen and talked about the formation of the hospice." Margaret Patton had completed a course in palliative care and she and Gerry began to gather around them like-minded people who wanted to raise money for the hospice.

Gerry recollected, "There was Séamus and Anna Mullan, Beth McElhinny, Barbara McClintock and James O'Brien. George Summers and myself later became members of the hospice committee. We were all active but aware of our limited local boundaries in Prehen. We talked to people and did letter drops. We had coffee mornings and held dances, and our cooking demonstrations were very successful.

"Tom was aware of my active involvement in the Glendermott Parish draw which was, at the time, raising £100,000 a year. He came for advice about a similar-type draw for the hospice and wondered whether our group would be interested in setting it up and then take full responsibility for running it. We agreed as a group to take it on. George Summers, who was a bank manager, was our treasurer. Standing orders were encouraged which helped a lot in the smooth running of the whole operation. Banks agreed not to charge for direct debits. Initially a car draw was an integral part of the Weekly Draw, and those who paid a year's subscription in advance could enter for the prize of a car. This was a huge extra prize annually. The first Weekly Draw took place on 12th December, 1985 in Crawford Square, with a first prize of £1000. It was a great night after all the work setting it up."

Unfortunately James O'Brien died the next day and our group was devastated. "From then on," said Gerry, "the Prehen Branch concentrated on the draw and other events gradually became fewer in number. In this way, we avoided

Foyle Hospice annual dinner dance in the Everglades Hotel. (From left) Anna and Séamus Mullan, Doreen and Jim Guy, Tom and Deirdre McGinley, and David and Angela McIntyre. A draw for a car took place at this dance on 1st December, 1987.

'milking' people who were getting 'charity fatigue'. There was a great deal of work involved in running the draw. Having a tax inspector in the group meant attention to detail and accuracy. Then, after Alistair died, my overall responsibility for the draw ceased."

The Weekly Draw is still the backbone of fundraising and is now overseen by Ciarán McGinley. The hospice is extremely indebted to the Prehen Group for setting it up and running it successfully for many years. Without the draw the raising of sufficient funds would have been extremely difficult.

The Prehen Branch Christmas Dinner, 1989. (From left) Séamus Mullan, Gerry Conaghan, George Summers, Michael Brown.

(From left) Winnie Brown, Margaret Patton, Barbara McClintock, Anna Mullan, Gerry Patton, Gerry Conaghan.

The Eglinton Support Group
Founded 1986-87

Founders of the group Maureen Craig and Rosemary O'Donnell with John McGill.

In 1983, Dr Maureen Craig (née Howie) was working in anaesthetics in Altnagelvin Hospital. It was inevitable she would meet Dr Tom who was also working in the same speciality. Naturally the subject of a hospice came up.

He suggested the setting up of a support group in the Eglinton area. Maureen is someone who is a 'doer' and she got started with Val Greenwood, Rosemary O'Donnell and Joan Cheetam who is now a volunteer in the Hospice Daycare Centre. Another stalwart member of the group, in the early days, was Margaret Keys whose husband Harry had died of leukaemia in 1984. He had worked as Chief Pharmacist alongside Deirdre McGinley in Altnagelvin Hospital. Sadly, Margaret herself died with cancer in September, 2004.

The group really got started in 1986-87 and made a goal of raising money for specific projects. In fact, once the Inpatient Unit was completed, they were responsible for furnishing the Chapel.

The popular jacuzzi, in the main hospice, was also funded by the Eglinton Group. More recently they funded the fittings for the kitchen in the Day Centre.

Members of the Eglinton Support Group presenting a cheque for £10,000 to Dr McGinley.

Their money was raised from jumble sales, coffee mornings and selling Christmas cards. Even now, in and around Eglinton, groups will run events and bring the proceeds to Maureen or Rosemary for passing on to the main hospice funds.

In 1989, they found a 'gem' in the shape of John McGill. He used to run Antiques Fairs in the White Horse Inn, giving the proceeds to various charities. He then decided to focus on raising funds for Foyle Hospice. All the door money is donated. The group, now in the form of Maureen and Rosemary, sell cards at this function. Maureen says, "They have now been running consistently, five times a year, for fifteen years. They raise the profile of the hospice and many people come from all over the North-West."

The Eglinton Group may be small but it is very active.

Limavady Support Group
Founded in January 1988

The group was kick-started in July 1987, when Bernadette was a Marie Curie nurse. In this role she was nursing Harold McFarland. Hannah Healy, Hospice Homecare Sister, was attending in her advisory capacity. This was Bernadette's first contact with the hospice.

A committee was formed with Bernadette as chairperson. Other members were Marie Keown, Christina McCartney, Roy King and Dorothy Nicholl. The group first met in January 1988. Alistair Kincaid, fundraiser from the hospice, was present.

(From left) Bernadette Campbell, founder of the group,
Marie Keown, Christina McCartney.

Once the group established themselves, they organised dances, fashion shows, quizzes, and took a stall at Christmas Fares. They also did house-to-house and street collections. Though now basically three in number, the group still raise about £8500 every year. Bernadette Campbell has now retired from nursing. All three are determined that the group will still continue to support the essential work of the hospice.

The Strabane Support Group
Founded in 1988

Maura McElroy and her husband Joe were driving through Derry one day when there happened to be a Female Hospice Run in progress, organised by Dr Tom McGinley. She explained to Joe what the Foyle Hospice was all about. Maura had been a nurse on the Eye Ward in St Columb's Hospital and had contact with Dr Tom. He had introduced her to hospice philosophy.

"I would like to get involved in that," said Joe. He was a man of action and soon got a group together. Ongoing events were now to start in Strabane for the hospice. Maura said, "My mother had died in Altnagelvin in 1977 from cancer of the colon. It really motivated him to raise money for Foyle Hospice."

Joe was a member of the Strabane District Council and persuaded them to donate an annual sum of £2000 to the hospice on an ongoing basis. Maura recollects, "He took part in the London and the Dublin marathons and walked from Dublin to Strabane, taking him seven days."

Maura McElroy (widow of Joe), and her sister-in-law, Bridget McElroy.

The support group has been working for 16 years. Bridget and her husband Patsy, Joe's brother, are now the main motivating force behind the group. Maura lends a hand as much as she can. Dolores McCafferty, another lady inspired by Joe, gives great assistance. Her "bubbliness and light-heartedness" motivates the group, says Bridget who, herself, walked the New York Marathon, raising over £2,500. All these ongoing activities to raise funds for the hospice are keeping the memory of Joe McElroy alive, who had said to his wife those many years ago, "I'd like to get involved in that." Joe McElroy died in July 1992 in the hospice.

Joe and Maura McElroy attend the 'Donegal Person of the Year' awards ceremony at the Grand Hotel, Malahide, in March 1992, when Dr McGinley received his award. (From left) Brendan Duddy, Maura and Joe McElroy, Margo Duddy, Ken and Helen McGilloway, Larry Doherty and Bernadette Mount. Larry was responsible for many of the photographs relating to the hospice which appeared in the Derry Journal.

The Dungiven & Feeny Support Group
Founded in 1992

Geraldine Brolly still lives Dungiven's main street. Her husband, Damien, was the first male patient admitted to the hospice. She remembers well the result of a biopsy he had in the spring of 1987. "We were both shocked when the result came back. It was Hodgkin's disease. Thank God he went into remission. Even knowing the diagnosis, we decided to marry in 1988. It was strange. The idea of him dying from this disease never entered my mind."

Then in 1991, Damien had a relapse of his cancer. "We were just aware of the hospice," Geraldine said. "I asked Damien's GP if he could be considered for the hospice. He had a lot of pain and vomiting. Dr McGinley took him in at that time to control his symptoms.

"He was admitted on 12th November, 1991 and given a single room. He was in about a week then came home for a while. He went in and out for several months before finally coming home in early February 1992. He loved being admitted to the hospice because he knew he would get relief from his symptoms. Staff used to remark about Damien's pleasant smile. I was very thankful to Mary McDaid, who was a volunteer, for looking after our young son Nicholas, while I sat with Damien. She played with him. He was asked to switch on the first Christmas lights at the hospice. He also presented a book to the Duchess of Norfolk when she visited the unit. When Damien came home for the last time, family members were most helpful at night so that I could get some sleep. If it wasn't for my faith I wouldn't have come through it. The whole experience of Damien's death brought me closer to my parents and his family." Then she said, "Near to the end I prayed for his release."

Dr Tom McGinley receiving a cheque for £1,600 from Geraldine Brolly, secretary of the Dungiven & Feeny Foyle Hospice Support Group. Included in the picture are members of the support group. This was the proceeds of their guest tea held in March 1995.

Three days before his death, a close friend, John Murphy, brought a minibus that could take a wheelchair, and took him down to Portrush where he really wanted to visit. He had chicken from KFC and some chips. Later they joked and called it his 'Last Supper'. He had not shaved for several days and when he came home he had a shave and went to bed. On the 28th February, he celebrated his birthday. He got a huge number of cards and a cake in the shape of a castle made from ice-cream cones. On the next day, 29th February, he died peacefully surrounded by his family."

Geraldine explained, "Soon after, Mum and I began thinking of raising money for the hospice because their work is so necessary. A guest tea was run in March 1995 and raised a large sum.

"We set up an official group with officers and a constitution. This ran for a number of years. The copper-hunt boxes were spread far and wide throughout Dungiven and are still collected today ten years on. We sell tickets for the Easter draw as well as any car draw. I'm still a promoter and have 30 members! Recently my Mum and I ran a National Coffee Morning and we raised more than £600 for Foyle Hospice."

Geraldine still finds the hospice most welcoming and homely.

"I like going to the interdenominational service at Christmas because we all share the same emotions. Grief is no respecter of persons."

She and her mother still work hard for the hospice.

Chapter Three

Pioneers of Hospice Homecare

Foyle Hospice premises at 9 Crawford Square. This was bought in March 1985.

Once the premises at Crawford Square had been purchased in March 1985, for the sum of £30,000, the decision to appoint two homecare nurses became a priority. It was felt that the logical path was to establish a homecare team first before commencing an inpatient unit. Adverts were placed in the local press for two nurses, ideally with community nursing experience. Unfortunately none of the applicants was found suitable. Tom discussed the situation with his health visitors in the Aberfoyle Practice, Helena Byrne and Margaret McLaughlin. They suggested that Hannah Walsh would be a suitable person for the post. She was, at that time, a district nurse working for a local GP practice. One day Hannah saw an advert. "I didn't know much about hospice care," she said. "I was going to apply but then didn't. I was frightened I could not do it as I was a 'softie' at heart and worried I'd be in tears all the time." Then Helena Byrne, a health visitor in Aberfoyle Practice, rang her, as suggested, to ask her to come and see Dr Tom. Hannah felt flattered and went to see him in his surgery. "He was very persuasive and resolved all my concerns." Encouraged by this encounter, she decided to 'drop Rosemary in it' and said that Nurse Rosemary Houston, who was working with her as a district nurse, might also be interested. Tom had known Rosemary when she had been a ward sister in Orthopaedics in Altnagelvin Hospital.

He was delighted to have a second nurse. Once both confirmed their acceptance, he explained they would have to do six weeks on a specialist course on

Clare Brennan, with her mother Colette, presents a cheque for £700 to Dr McGinley for the hospice. Hannah (left) met the family during her time in Birmingham. The money came from various events organised by Clare, at her school in Birmingham. Her father had died previously from cancer in Birmingham and donations, in lieu of flowers, came to Foyle Hospice. Her granny was 90 years old recently and donations, in lieu of her birthday gifts, also came to the hospice. (See Picture Gallery)

Some of the GPs who attended the launch in February 1986. (From left) Dr John Hart, Dr Brendan McCartie, Dr Charlie O'Sullivan, Ms Flanagan, Dr McGinley, and Dr Morris Browne. Morris gave sustained support for the hospice over the years together with the people in Castlederg.

Care of the Dying. Dr McGinley was able to secure places for two nurses to be trained almost immediately although, at that time, it was nearly impossible to get placements on these popular courses. This was due to Tom's contacts at St Mary's and St Joseph's Hospice.

Hannah went to St Mary's in Birmingham. After six weeks she joined Rosemary, who had now started at St Joseph's, for a further five weeks.

When they returned to Derry, they were both full of enthusiasm and keen to get started. They were further delighted when 80 GPs turned up on 5th February, 1986 for a meeting in Crawford Square to explain their role. They showed enormous support and enthusiasm for the new service. Both Hannah and Rosemary felt that this huge support was due in no small measure to the fact that Dr Tom was a GP himself and most knew him personally. Both Hannah and Rosemary had been active and well-known district nurses and this also helped. This hugely successful meeting became the official launch of homecare.

Some months after the meeting with GPs, clergy of all denominations were invited to Crawford Square. In the June edition of the Limavady Parish Bulletin, Father Kevin Mullan wrote positively about that meeting.

> "Dr Tom McGinley with nurses Rosemary and Hannah held an information session for the clergy of all denominations in the catchment

area. Dr Tom spoke of the old Irish way of death where the neighbours took a great interest in the dying person, their last words, and saw death as part of a natural cycle of life. Now death occurs in isolation, in lonely rooms, and people are blamed if someone dies – it is seen as an intrusion into life.

"The hospice team tries to bring back the 'team care' for the dying, uniting medical, spiritual, emotional elements in the process. They attempt to alleviate distress; to control pain where pain has no meaning because the disease is terminal. They try to communicate deeply with the person and talk about dying. They share their understanding with the medical staff already attending the sick person and they provide a homecare service, because many see home as the place to die. They are introducing us to a concept of care in a caring community, and help us look death in the face. They hope to give the dying person dignity and give them some control over what is happening. They value truth and respect in dealing with the sick and go wherever they are asked to help. They can deal with up to 30 patients at present."

Dr McGinley referred the first patient to Rosemary and Hannah. This was Berna McLaughlin. Soon another patient, Paula Robinson, was also referred and the service began in earnest.

Memories of those early days
Hannah Walsh

"We found most GPs to be very helpful and receptive. A few, however, had great difficulty in accepting *MST* (slow-release-Morphine) which only needed to be taken every 12 hours. One of our earliest tasks was to counteract the fear of using adequate doses of morphine. All this was done, of course, for the comfort of the patient and full control of their pain. Initially there were some difficulties arising with nurses in communicating this new information. It was always made quite clear to GPs that our role was advisory and that they remained in sole charge. Some GPs regarded increasing doses of morphine akin to euthanasia! Gradually they became more receptive to our advice.

"The introduction of the syringe driver at that time was an extremely useful innovation, allowing for the slow release of medication over a 24 hour period. It was greatly beneficial for those who had difficulties in swallowing their oral medication.

The first TV broadcast about Foyle hospice. RTE is here recording Hannah and Rosemary as they explain how the syringe-driver works. (March 1988)

"We felt that the driver made a vast difference for the control of pain and other symptoms, especially in the final days of a person's life. Initially it was seen by a few people as something that was erected as part of the last rites!

"Dr Tom was always keen we should be able to visit patients with advanced cancer in hospital, especially prior to going home. The hospital did not permit this early on. He was also of the opinion that a specialist nurse in palliative care should be appointed in the hospital. When we were first accepted into the hospital to advise the nurses, we felt threatened somewhat. We would speak to nursing staff but they were very reluctant to sanction anything. The Homecare Nurse now attends weekly meetings at the hospital prior to the discharge of patients."

Hannah has 20 years experience, arguably longer than any other homecare nurse in the British Isles. She is still greatly loved and appreciated by the hundreds of patients and relatives she has been associated with. She still loves her work and finds great satisfaction in trying to ease the symptoms of those in need of palliative care, as well as their families, in the security of their own homes. "It is still very difficult for me at times," she says. "I recently attended a 19-year-old boy with terminal cancer. I thought of Dr Tom's experience of dealing with a boy of similar age so many years ago."

Mrs Kathleen Heaney cooked for staff in Crawford Square during those early years. She was a cheery face who was greatly appreciated by everyone. Kathleen's husband James died of cancer at home attended by Dr Tom and Rosemary. Previously, he had walked the 1985 Derry City Marathon with 'Whitey' O'Neill, a well-known local character, raising a large sum in sponsorship for the hospice. Kathleen also featured on the RTE programme, when she talked about her husband's illness, death and her feelings of bereavement.

Helen McMahon, Rosemary, Hannah, and Gretta Linehan with the nursing advisor, Angela McIntyre and Dr Tom McGinley, Medical Director. The four nursing sisters made up the homecare nursing team in the late 1980s.

Rosemary Peoples

Rosemary recalls her time in Altnagelvin Hospital where she first met Dr McGinley. "He used to call in every Thursday evening to examine the patients for the next morning's orthopaedic operating list. He was also able to give advice for patients on the ward who had difficult pain problems due to advanced cancer. I remember particularly a patient of Tom's from Barry Street who had widespread bony secondaries. He had been treating her at home very successfully with a drug called Temgesic. This drug was not available except on a named-patient basis and the supply had to come from England. The great benefits were that it could be taken under the tongue. During the last few years this drug has made a comeback and is now used as a patch for non-malignant chronic pain.

"I enjoyed my time in St Joseph's and subsequently I went to the Dorothy House Foundation for a few weeks for extra experience in homecare. This hospice was in Bath, near Bristol where Tom was no stranger to the staff.

"Once Hannah and I were established in Crawford Square, we were invited to visit patients in many parts of Donegal as well as locally. In fact, our cross-border visits went as far as Dungloe in West Donegal. One patient who sticks in my memory lived in Letterkenny. He was a patient of Dr James McDaid. Adrian was only six and was absolutely terrified of the injection for his pain. Tom and I decided to use the syringe-driver as being the only appropriate measure to relieve his pain. This gave complete relief to him, and when he died a short time later he was peaceful and pain-free. This was the first time a syringe-driver was used for a child in homecare. The care we gave to that little boy became the catalyst for the formation of the Donegal Hospice Group."

Dr Vincent Cavanagh
Aberfoyle Practice

"All the doctors strongly approved and supported the hospice project as it moved from the drawing board to the provision of homecare sisters from the Crawford Square premises. Our district nurses, the strength and bedrock of care in the community, also found that these newly trained hospice nurses were of enormous help and were absolutely not rivals. They all worked together along with Marie Curie nurses to bring care, calmness and skill, night and day, to many households and families."

Gretta Linehan
Homecare Sister, Nurse-in-Charge (Night Duty)

Gretta Linehan has suffered more than her share of grief. This, she says, has helped her to develop empathy for those suffering loss. "The biggest grief of my life," she said, "was the loss of Terri, my seven-year-old daughter. She was killed in 1980 in a farming accident. Our first child, Patrick, born in 1974 developed meningitis when he was only six weeks old. We were told Patrick would not talk, walk or see. Later he went to Fleming Fulton Special School, and I insisted he was integrated into society and not hidden away."

Gretta was encouraged to return to work and joined the Marie Curie Foundation. During the course of her work she met Dr Tom. "What impressed me was Dr Tom called with patients who were terminally ill every night even when off duty." She became familiar with Hannah and Rosemary in homecare during her period with Marie Curie. She became familiar with 'this new thing' called a syringe driver. "Dr Tom had organised talks for Marie Curie nurses at Crawford Square. After one of these talks he asked to speak to me. At first I wondered what I'd done wrong. What in fact he wanted was to ask me to do the course on 'Care of the Dying' at St Gemma's Hospice in Leeds. He explained that as Rosemary was about to get married and would be off for a few weeks, there would be a vacancy for a locum to cover her work." Gretta went on to say, "Well! Before I finally agreed to go, I made every excuse in the book. I explained I'd been too long away from the books; I would be leaving

Gretta's daughter, Terri, who died in 1980.

my children; I couldn't fly – I hate it; finally, in desperation I said, 'I'm too old and anyway I'd get lost', as I'd never been away from home before." Angela McIntyre tried to persuade her as well. Even her husband was in support of the suggestion. Finally, in fear and trepidation, she went in February 1987. "In fact I enjoyed the course immensely," she said.

Once trained, she provided locum cover for Hannah and Rosemary. She worked a longer period when Rosemary was off having her first baby.

Another first for Gretta was the fact she had to learn to drive. She passed her test on the very first day of her homecare duties. "Once the hospice opened, Rosemary went to the Inpatient Unit and I was on my own for a while when Hannah got married. Then, of all things, I had a car accident just outside the hospice gate and demolished part of the newly built wall! I got bruised ribs but the car was a write-off."

She continued working with Hannah but kept up her Marie Curie contact. "I loved working at night. I felt more alive and always thought that the quiet of the night was a time when people could unload or speak more openly. Then I was interviewed for an inpatient post in the hospice when Teresa McSwiney came out to work in homecare. I went on doing full-time night duty from 1992 and was in charge at night."

Gretta retired as a hospice nurse in 2001. She became involved in the *Forget-me-Not* bereavement support group. It was organised for relatives of those who had died and it meets in the hospice three times a year. Invitations go out to all relatives. She acts as facilitator, not a counsellor, she was careful to explain. Gretta continues to work as a volunteer in the hospice.

The 'white-haired' night sister!

Angela McIntyre
Trustee and nursing advisor

Tragedy touches most lives at some time. Angela and her husband David were no exception. On 14th December 1979, Angela bore twins, Laura and Emma who both suffered from a rare genetic disease called Rhett's Syndrome. They were profoundly physically and mentally handicapped. Then, as fate would have it, Angela bore a second set of twins, Ruth and David. Unfortunately baby David died on 26th September 1986 from a cot-death. Both she and her husband David were devastated.

Angela had many a 'chat' with God. How could He let this happen? Even today Angela cannot work on 26th September. Then, some years later, Laura became very ill in May 1994 and died in Altnagelvin Hospital. Again the family was plunged into grief.

Laura's twin, Emma, is now 26 years old, and, though severely handicapped, is a very happy child and greatly loved by all the family.

Angela had been a health visitor in the community for many years and subsequently has become a lecturer in Child Care and Health at the North-West Institute. Her first introduction to plans for a local hospice was during 1982 when Dr Tom was attending her for hepatitis.

He also called regularly to see her twins. Angela says, "He would often talk about the lack of quality time for patients who were dying of advanced cancer.

"One day I heard the doctor speak about cancer with my husband David. I thought they were talking about me!" she said, "I was most relieved when I found out it wasn't true. But, you know, in those days, often people would walk away from dying people in the hospital."

Angela recollected her early days in nursing. "A dying man asked me to stay

David who died suddenly on 26th September, 1986, aged 3 months.

Laura and Emma with Paula in the middle. (1980)

with him and hold his hand. I was a student nurse. I went and asked the sister if I could stay. She said no, because there were other matters to be attended to on the ward. She told me that I could go back afterwards. When I went back he was dead. That was 1966. It left a deep impression on me."

After her recovery from hepatitis, Dr Tom kept discussing his plans for a hospice and was waiting for the right time to launch it. "The following year after the initial launch I was very keen to get involved in fundraising and began helping Don and Celine Carlin who were setting up the first support group in William Street." Angela was a great support to them. "I was heavily involved in the very first flag day. In fact the money was counted in our house. Then Crawford Square was bought in '85 and Hannah and Rosemary came 'on line' so to speak. We all helped to decorate the rooms.

"I was also responsible for organising the ACE workers. This was a government run and funded scheme. Such great workers for the hospice as Bernadette, Joan, Terri and Marcella all came via that scheme. They were allowed to work for a year but sometimes we could negotiate them staying on another three to six months. Then, after the scheme was over, some were invited to stay on. Paddy 'Bogside' Doherty was heavily involved in this."

Angela has never ceased working for the hospice and today is an active member of the Trustees and advisor in nursing matters.

Chapter Four

Race for the Site

Fundraising had been curtailed due to the Ethiopian famine crisis during 1985. This gave the committee time to concentrate on the future development of the hospice. Now that homecare was firmly established and completely accepted by GPs as well as the community, the next step was to plan for an inpatient unit. This purpose-built unit would be required to provide beds for symptom control as well as for respite care. Many would be admitted for the terminal stage of their illness. An all-out fundraising campaign was planned. It was thought that the community, as a whole, would spontaneously respond once definite plans of a building could be seen.

From the very beginning, Tom felt that the newly built Foyle Bridge should be in full view of the proposed hospice building. By this stage the National Society for Cancer Relief [subsequently renamed the Macmillan Fund] had agreed to fund the homecare sisters for two years. These were welcome finances. It was doubly satisfying that the hospice had been recognised for the excellent work of the established homecare team by such a prestigious organisation.

In June 1986, Professor Eric Wilkes, Chairman of *Help the Hospices*, was invited to Derry. He was delighted to be a guest of Tom and Deirdre in their home. Tom and Brendan Duddy took him to see some of the beautiful scenery in Donegal. While visiting Derry, Prof Wilkes delivered a public lecture at Magee College as well as meeting hospice staff at Crawford Square. He was also interviewed by Radio Foyle on their afternoon programme. He lent his total support for the local hospice project. These two events helped to boost the public profile of the hospice.

Tom had spent some time, during the previous year, at St Luke's Hospice in Sheffield where Prof Wilkes was the medical director. He was impressed by the input that one general practice team had into the ongoing medical cover of the hospice. During that visit Tom was taken to see a full time palliative care specialist nurse working in the acute general hospital in Sheffield. She liaised very closely with homecare nurses. Tom later approached the nursing officer in the local Western Health Board and suggested such a post be established at Altnagelvin. Foyle Hospice would be prepared to fund this post for the first year. If it had proved successful, it was suggested by him that the Board continue funding. Unfortunately this wasn't to happen, though happily the North Western Health Board in Donegal were prepared to fund such a post completely and it was advertised at the time.

A course on *Communicating with the Dying and Relatives* took place in Magee College that Autumn.

Everything was going well. The public was beginning to grasp the vision. Finding a site now became urgent. Tom looked carefully at land on the Culmore Road. Much of this land designated was in a green belt area where it might be very difficult or impossible to acquire planning permission for a hospice.

Dr Brendan O'Hare, then a medical student with the Aberfoyle Practice, remembers Tom taking him down to the Culmore Road and pointing to the site where the hospice stands today. He said, "That's where the hospice will be built." Brendan subsequently became a great supporter of the work of the hospice and is, today, a GP Macmillan Facilitator.

Bill Doherty of WJ McMonagle & Co Ltd. (Building Contractors) takes up the story.

"Tom was my doctor at the Aberfoyle Practice. Our offices were on Strand Road and I was a director of the company. Tom often called at our office on his way home from evening surgery. He was very friendly with Larry Boyle, our office manager. Even at that time, Tom talked a lot about the need for some kind of extra local service for terminally ill patients. Sadly, Larry died in August 1976 while jogging with Tom and his son Ciarán on their favourite beach in west Donegal.

"He arranged to see me on the Culmore Road in late 1985. He discussed his plans for a hospice. Tom already had his mind set on the Boomhall area as he felt, with the completion of the new Foyle Bridge, it would be a neutral location. He was aware that I had leased land from the Orange Order in that area. They owned about 40 acres. It had been used for 12th July celebrations, but not since 1969. He was well versed with the Area Plan (1981-96). He was hopeful the planners would look kindly at an application to build a hospice. He was also aware that, further out in the Ballynagard area, planning permission for houses had been turned down, despite the businessmen involved having sought support from local politicians for the their application. The

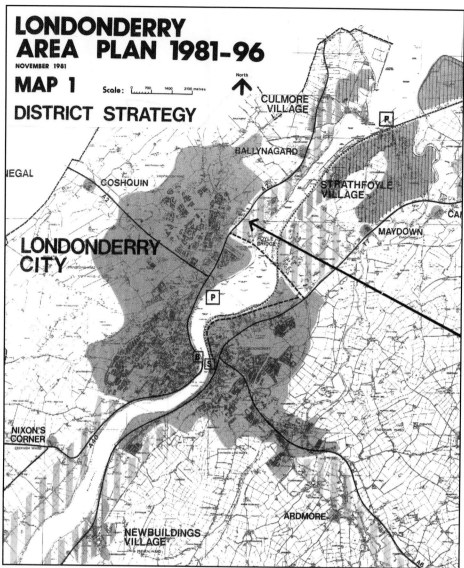

The striped yellow areas indicate land where housing would not be permitted.
The arrow points to the area where the hospice was eventually built.

Orange Order themselves, he knew, had applied unsuccessfully for housing development on their land through a third party. I explained that Tommy McBride and the Pennyburn Youth Club also owned land in that area. The club had, at one time, plans for a football pitch on their land. Tom approached the planning office to seek permission to build a hospice on the club site. After a few visits they agreed to his request provided an access road was created from the Culmore Road."

Brendan Duddy recalls standing on the hollow and waterlogged site:

"Tom mentioned to me that he was going to approach the Orange Order about road access through their land. I replied, 'Tom you have no chance'. 'No chance' was a phrase which didn't seem to exist in his vocabulary. At this moment another side of him showed itself to me. He turned around sharply and confronted me. 'I bet you're wrong,' he said and he suggested a certain bet. I told him that I wasn't a betting man but I agreed to a small wager. The topic wasn't mentioned further until a few weeks later, while out running, when he casually turned to me and said, 'Brendan, put the money that you lost on that bet in a hospice box!' (Today he'd probably have asked me to Gift-Aid it as well!) The Orange Order had granted his request and planning permission was confirmed."

Bill Doherty continues:

"Some time after our previous meeting, Tom rang to say the Pennyburn Youth Club site had been bought and planning permission granted. I asked Tom, 'When are you starting to build? 'That's what I actually want to talk to you about,' he said. We arranged to meet on the site. I explained to Tom that a main sewer ran across that land. I was astonished at his immediate reply. 'Fantastic,' he said, 'we

Dr McGinley on the Pennyburn Youth Club site, purchased in June 1986.

can tell the public that sorting out that problem will cause a delay.' It then became obvious that he never had any intention whatsoever of building on that hollow site. Suddenly it dawned on me what he was up to. It was an excuse to test the planners. Another delaying action he had already used was to arrange for an architect's competition which was going to take some time to organise. Tom then turned to me and said, 'I want you to introduce me to Tommy McBride.'"

Tommy owned six acres above the newly acquired hospice site and was known by Bill Doherty personally for quite some time. "He used to own a butcher's shop on Strand Road," said Bill. "In fact he was famous for a sign he had on the gable wall of his shop,

'ALWAYS PLEASED TO MEET YOU – ALWAYS MEAT TO PLEASE YOU'

"I arranged a meeting between Tommy McBride and the doctor who would subsequently pay many visits to his house in Kingsfort Park. Initially he was reluctant to sell land he was using for grazing. A deal was eventually struck at a price well above the going rate for agricultural land. Tom felt, however, that it was well worth the extra cost."

The deal was completed in January 1988. Tommy McBride rang Bill later. "McGinley's a very persistent man," he said, "I was getting worried the neighbours would think I had cancer as his car was parked outside the house so often! He even hinted one evening that the people of Derry would not forgive me if I didn't sell him the land for the hospice site."

Some time later Tom proceeded to purchase a further six acres from the Orange Order.

Plans had been started during 1987 for an architects' competition. This was used as a delaying tactic until further land would be acquired from Tommy McBride as already mentioned. Architects throughout the North-West were circulated with the details of the competition and nearly all entered. The Chief Assessor was David Huchinson, ARIBA, of Hutchinson, Locke and Monk, Richmond, Surrey.

He had won the Civic Trust Award for his own design of the Princess Alice Hospice in Esher. A second assessor was also appointed who was Ian Campbell of Campbell & Partners of Belfast. Brendan Duddy takes up the story, "Tom invited me to accompany him on a trip to London in October 1987. He visited a few hospices in London including St Joseph's in Hackney. His main aim, however, was to visit the Chief Assessor for the architectural competition. His office was in Richmond, Surrey. We then went to visit the Princess Alice

Area 'A': The site purchased originally from Pennyburn Youth Club site.

'a': This interrupted line shows the small strip of access land acquired from the Orange Order.

Area 'B': The McBride field.

Arrow 1: Where land-fill was placed by WJ McMonagle & Co Ltd. as evidence that work had already started on the site.

Area 'C': The Orange Order land.

Area 'D': The Foyle Hospice site, after the rest of the land was sold back to Derry City Council

1: Inpatient Unit

2: Hospice Day Centre

'b': The access road to both the Inpatient Unit and the Day Centre

Arrow 2: This indicates the point where the historic boom had been erected to protect the fortified City of Derry. It was broken in July 1689 ending the 105 day siege.

Dr McGinley in Surrey with the Chief Assessor David Hutchinson ARIBA

Hospice in Esher. Tom made a mental note of all the pluses and the minuses with regard to the unit. I say 'mental' because he never took notes. On our way back to Heathrow we witnessed the start of the great storm in the south of England on the 15th October, 1987. Trees were being blown down everywhere. An unequalled 15 million trees were lost and 18 people were killed. London lost power for the first time since the Blitz. We were lucky, at that time, to get a flight out of Heathrow."

The McBride land had been purchased in January 1988. In May of that year a large crowd walked from Crawford Square to the new site on the Culmore Road. On the 24th May the musical, 'Starchild', written and produced by TC Doherty, held its premier. This raised substantial funds for the hospice. The architects' competition continued throughout 1988.

Then in November, Tom addressed Derry City Council's Finance and General Purposes Committee. The outcome was reported in the *Derry Journal* on 18th November. The headline read:

£30,000 COMMITMENT FROM FINANCE COMMITTEE
FOYLE HOSPICE GETS FULL BACKING

The article went on to say:

DERRY CITY'S Finance and General Purposes Committee has agreed to give Foyle Hospice £30,000 over the next two years.

The commitment came after local doctor Tom McGinley, addressed the committee to appeal for financial aid this week. Dr McGinley said

Meantime people were walking and running to raise the large sums needed. This was the annual sponsored walk from Crawford Square which ended at the site. (May 1988)

Above, the walk passing along Northland Road, and below, returning from the site

it was hoped to have work on the new one million pound hospice started next summer. It was to be built on the Culmore Road, near the new Foyle Bridge, and its running costs each year would be in the region of £400,000.

Explaining the function of the hospice, Dr McGinley said it was not just somewhere people went to die but was a place where very great care could be given to those suffering pain.

"We consider people as much as the disease they are suffering," he said. He commented that, due to the heavy financial costs involved, he was making approaches in several areas in order to get aid. One of the 'big guns' he said he was approaching was the City Council. He wanted the council "to help us make the hospice a success".

Many councillors paid tribute to the work of Dr McGinley. It was one of the few times when representatives of all political parties actually agreed with one another!

A large crowd of walkers on the site at Culmore Road. The banner advertises the fifth musical by TC Doherty, 'Starchild'. All proceeds went to Foyle Hospice.

SDLP councillors Joe Fegan, Annie Courtney and Pat Devine were also glowing in their praise of the hospice and the work of Dr McGinley, while Sinn Fein's Mitchel McLaughlin said he wanted to put on record his congratulations to Dr McGinley and his team for the great work they were doing. The DUP's William Hay also remarked that the hospice was carrying out admirable work.

Towards the end of 1988, the final six architects were shortlisted. Architects Smith & McMurtry of Limavady were the unanimous choice and a model of the future building was unveiled at the Art Gallery in Derry on 5th December, 1988. Everyone thought the hospice would be now built on McBride's field. Bill Doherty met Tom on the night of the launch and said to him, "You must be a happy man now. You've got the land you wanted." He called me aside and whispered, "There could be another twist in the tale yet!" I had no idea what he was talking about.

Approaches had been made to the Northern Ireland Department of Health for funding but they announced that they would not be contributing to funds for the hospice. Dr Tom was quoted in an article in the *Derry Journal* by Seamus McKinney:

> "Despite repeated approaches by local bishops, MPs from here and in Britain including David Alton and Paddy Ashdown, Foyle Hospice will not qualify for any regional grant."

Unveiling the model on 5th December,1988. (From left) Jim Guy, Ian Campbell, Dr McGinley, Obie Smith, Mayor Annie Gallagher, Deirdre McGinley.

At this time, a member of the local Western Health and Social Services Board had an informal meeting with Dr McGinley to offer Anderson House as a possible building for the Foyle Hospice. It was a redundant building that had been a GP maternity unit in the heart of the Altnagelvin complex. Tom's immediate response was that this offer was a non-starter. It would not be suitable, as plans for Foyle Hospice were at an advanced stage on the Culmore Road. Architects had already been appointed. The Hospice Committee was unanimous in its decision not to accept the offer. However the Board still felt it necessary to make public announcements in the press. Tom was very concerned that, if the public were to see that we had refused a firm offer of a building, it might affect their attitude towards the fundraising campaign. He immediately went back to Bill Doherty.

"Tom landed at my door late one night rather agitated. 'Bill,' he said, 'the local health board is going to make a public announcement in the papers about their proposed offer of Anderson House for use as a hospice. I'm asking you for a big favour. I want to show some evidence to the public that work has commenced on the Culmore Road site. Please, please can you arrange to have as much landfill as possible dumped onto the site? Can you have evidence of machinery as well?' He told me he'd arrange a photograph. I told him I'd certainly help. Then Tom asked, 'There's only one problem. The photograph needs to be taken before the *Derry Journal* starts printing on Thursday night.' This was late on Tuesday night. We made an all-out effort. WJ McMonagle's lorries were seen delivering landfill from all over. On the Friday morning, the photograph appeared confirming that work on the Foyle Hospice site had started. In the same edition the possible offer of Anderson House, from the local Health Board, appeared. In the eyes of the public, the offer was no longer relevant. Some weeks later, in fact, a lady from the Waterside stopped me and said, 'Why couldn't they have made this offer before the hospice started work?'"

We now owned 16 acres of land. We had arranged road access to the site. We had unveiled a model of a hospice building and still had the public's confidence. In fact, everything was in place to go out to tender. But Tom was still not finished.

What was the need for further delay? Committee members were somewhat confused, as was the public.

The author later found out the truth. Tom wanted to buy the remaining 34 acres owned by the Orange Order. He realised that if he discussed it with the committee they would most likely not agree. (I was Vice-Chairman of that Committee!) He was, however, risking the fact that planners would not agree to rescind the original planning permission and permit relocation to the intended new site. There was a real possibility it could take up to two years. This would stall the entire operation.

Evidence that work had started! (From left) Thomas Ferguson (Orange Order), Douglas Caldwell (Secretary of the Londonderry Grand Orange Lodge), Alan Lindsay (Deputy Grand Master of the Londonderry Orange Lodge), David Cairns (Orange Lodge), Brian McCloskey (Foyle Hospice Solicitor), Tommy McBride, Robert Fleming (Grand Master of the Londonderry Orange Order), Dr Tom McGinley, Paul Doherty (W.J McMonagle & Sons Ltd.), Joe Scullion (Treasurer of Foyle Hospice).

The optimum site, for him, was still the one on which the hospice is now built. He realised it would require £200,000 to purchase, (perhaps £500,000 or more in today's prices). There could be no way that the hospice fund could afford this. The only way was to reach an agreement with the council that they would purchase the excess land not required for the needs of the hospice. Tom approached Cathal Logue, Chief Amenities Officer of Derry City Council, who was a patient and friend of Tom's and was aware of his plans to set up a hospice. Tom had worked very closely with his department, as their medical advisor, during the many marathons held in the early 1980s. He also knew many of the councillors personally. He suggested to Cathal that the excess land would be ideal for the council to purchase as open park land.

Cathal approached the recreation committee of the council who brought the proposal to the full city council. It endorsed Tom's suggestion and approached the Department of the Environment for funding to buy the excess land. They agreed to jointly fund the purchase. Jim Guy was a vital catalyst in all of these arrangements. He was a keen supporter of the hospice and later became a

Trustee. The council was pleased with this arrangement as it was now able to protect this area from future developments as well as facilitating the hospice. The council's plan subsequently was to develop the land into a county park similar to St Columb's in the Waterside, whenever money became available. Tom subsequently suggested that the council purchase a number of acres that lay between the hospice and the Culmore Road. They were happy with the idea and laid out that area with dense tree cover which now adds significantly to privacy and gives shelter to the hospice.

He went to see representatives of the Derry Grand Lodge of the Orange Order who consulted and agreed to sell the other 34 acres of land to Foyle Hospice. Their solicitor, Don McClay, was most helpful and supportive.

Tom was keen to clinch the deal as quickly as possible as he was aware that there was a possibility that a third party would buy that land and exchange it for land on the opposite side of the Culmore Road where no planning restrictions existed.

It was agreed that a deposit of £10,000 would be accepted and the rest would be paid over two years. He rushed across to Brian McCloskey, the hospice solicitor, and presented him with his own personal cheque to be forwarded immediately to the Orange Order's solicitor. Brian was somewhat surprised at this sudden development. Later Tom's wife, Deirdre, remarked, "He probably had planned to use my pharmacy business as security against the cheque!"

Tom approached the Planning Office with a request to rescind the original planning permission and was turned down. It was explained to Tom that it

---

	27th June ··········.19.....89.
	Trustees City of Derry Grand Orange Lodge -to- Foyle Hospice.
Received from	Dr Tom Mc Ginley 4 Shandon Park, Derry.
the sum of	Ten thousand pounds.
For payment of deposit on purchase of lands at Ballynashallog, herein,	
	B. W. McCLOSKEY SOLICITOR 14 QUEEN STREET LONDONDERRY
£ 10,000. oo	

The receipt for the deposit

Dr Tom McGinley signing the contract for the purchase of the land for the hospice at Culmore Road, Derry, from the Londonderry Grand Orange Order. With Dr McGinley is Alan Lindsay, the Deputy Grand Master, and behind (from left) the late Brian McCloskey, hospice legal advisor, Douglas Caldwell, secretary, Londonderry Grand Orange Lodge, and Don McClay,(legal adviser for the Orange Order).

would take up to two years before that could be done. Tom would not take no for an answer!

He invited the Chief Planning Officer for the area, Arnold Bloomfield, to visit the proposed new site. Tom explained that after we built the main hospice the plan was, ideally, to add a Daycare Centre and relocate the fundraising premises from Crawford Square to the main hospice area. The original site would not have been large enough to facilitate these further proposed developments. Of greater importance, Tom went on to say, was the fact that the new site would now have a full view of the river and a full view of the bridge. This was at the very root of Foyle Hospice philosophy. Tom made a passionate plea to Arnold that any delay would be disastrous for the whole project. It was a gloriously sunny day and as he pointed out the significance of the river and the bridge, a big ship passed by. Tom was later to recall that Arnold turned to him and said, "I suppose you arranged this for my benefit?" Tom found him very understanding and most sympathetic to the hospice philosophy. A few days later he rang to confirm that the original planning permission had been rescinded. As a result the whole project could go full-steam ahead.

Tom called an emergency meeting of the hospice committee to explain that they were now the owners of an extra 34 acres of prime agricultural land. This brought the overall number of acres to 50. When all was explained, the committee was delighted. The architects were able to adjust their prize-winning plan to the new and much superior site.

Chapter Five

Building towards the Opening

The project went out to tender and Cregan Brothers were subsequently appointed as builders of the hospice. The cost of the building was estimated at £1.25 million. The launch of the Inpatient Building Project was held on 12th October, 1989 at 9 Crawford Square. This date was chosen especially by Tom, because it was his mother's birth date. She had died three years previously and had been such an influence on his education and thinking.

During the following month an article entitled "A Shared Prayer for the Dying" appeared in a Medical Journal written by local GP Michael Healy. The following are some extracts:

> It has taken Derry GP Dr Tom McGinley more than 20 years to fulfil his dream of building a hospice facility in the North West of Ireland.
>
> There have been many struggles on the road to achieving his goal of a homecare system for the dying and an inpatient building for treatment of the short term symptoms uncontrollable at home. In the setting of Northern Ireland, a country better known for its political and religious struggles, the problems have ranged from the mundane aspects of fundraising and planning permission to more deeply rooted heart-searching over location.
>
> One of the earliest problems was to convince the local medical and nursing community that such a facility was required. Four years on from the establishment of the Hospice Homecare service the mood has swung to "how did we ever do without them".
>
> Dr McGinley felt the location building had to be geographically, therapeutically and culturally perfect.
>
> The Foyle Hospice is unique in two aspects. First, it has almost entirely been funded by the local community with no funding from government. Second, the Foyle Hospice has shifted the focus of care

The launch of the plan for the Inpatient Unit held in Crawford Square (Oct 1989).

for the dying back into the hands of GPs and away from hospital specialists. Patients are referred to the hospice by their GPs. The patient is then visited by one of the three full-time homecare sisters who then reports back to the GP for discussion of the problems, scripts for drugs, requests for appliances and so on.

In this system, the family doctor still maintains ultimate responsibility for the patient yet every one of the caring team can benefit from the homecare sister's specialist involvement.

The 12-bed Inpatient Unit will also include family rooms, daycare facilities, an area for religious services and an educational unit.

Lesser mortals might have been scared away from such a project. And Dr McGinley was already a full-time partner in an urban practice of approximately 12,000 patients and a fully qualified anaesthetist doing three sessions a week. He believes, however, that "palliative care represents our point on the continuum of care for the dying which stretches right through from diagnosis, treatment and finally peaceful dignified death. It is the GP who is best placed to provide this care and it is our duty to do so".

The founding of any new organisation is always difficult, but one cannot help but be impressed at the tenacity of this organisation which has overcome many practical and philosophical problems to provide an invaluable service and succeed in uniting a community where the politicians have failed.

Robert Fleming, Grand Master of the Orange Order, presenting a £1000 symbolic brick to Dr McGinley.

Building commenced in January 1990. The idea of symbolic bricks was launched within a few weeks and the Orange Order agreed to present the Hospice with an initial 'brick' of £1000. Eventually a leather bound book was made to record the names of those who gave symbolic 'bricks' to the hospice as well as other donations.

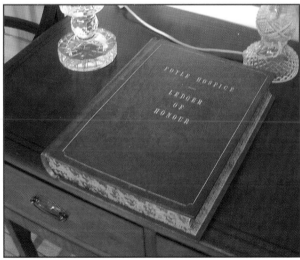

The Ledger of Honour kept on a table in the entrance hall of the hospice.

Lisa Glenn from Belmont had saved up all her pocket money to buy a symbolic brick. Here she is presenting her money to Dr Tom (family doctor). (Jan 1990)

Dr McGinley seated with George Cregan (Cregan Brothers, Building Contractors) signing the contract. (Standing from left) Jack McCauley,(quantity surveyor), Michael Cregan, Rodney Willis (Delap & Waller – Electrical & Mechanical engineers), Ian Warnock (structural engineer), Jim McMurtry (architect), Brian McCloskey (solicitor).

Dr Tom at the helm of the digger – lifting the first sod.

Dr McGinley with the Grand Master of the Orange Lodge, Robert Fleming, and the builders George and Michael Cregan. (January 1990)

Building work rapidly advancing during spring 1990.

It seemed destined that 1990-91 was to become a roller-coaster of a year. With the construction on target, further major fundraising was vital. The aim was to inform every household in the North-West and Inishowen about Foyle Hospice. A package was designed with a colour pamphlet and information on 'Ways of Giving'. About 35,000 were distributed by eager helpers. At the same time it was decided to write to Grant-Aiding Trusts to seek funding. Letters were written to 549 Trusts. £110,000 was added to the main fund as a result.

Artist's impression of the finished hospice building. This cover was used in publicity as well as being sent to 285 Trusts and Grant-Aiding bodies.

The relaxing area in one of the four-bedded rooms.

Conservatory financed by Dupont.

Suddenly the sad news of the death of our solicitor, Brian McCloskey was received. Tributes were paid by his fellow committee members for his years of work for Foyle Hospice. He gave selflessly of his time and expertise. Paddy Kelly, from the same legal firm, was subsequently appointed as the hospice solicitor.

During building, it became obvious to Tom that the two 4-bedded rooms had no suitable sitting-out area for the patients so they could enjoy the beautiful surroundings. The architects initially were reluctant to alter their design. Needless to say, the man from West Donegal got his way, and the alterations were made accordingly.

Another feature not in the original design was a conservatory. Dupont were approached with a request to finance this facility. They were most agreeable to the suggestion.

Eventually two young girls were chosen to perform the official opening of the hospice. Both their mothers had died from cancer and had been cared for by the homecare nurses. One was a Protestant and one a Catholic. They were now aged

Councillor Mary Bradley receiving the first spray of 'Forget-Me-Not' flowers from Bernie Mount from 'Glendinnings'. The community were encouraged to wear these during Hospice Week (15th-22nd June). Included is Dr Tom McGinley with a bouquet of flowers to be distributed by the Mayor to local councillors.

eight and were delighted to be invited. Their names were Emma Robinson and Clare McLaughlin.

By April, Mid-Ulster Gardens had begun landscaping the gardens. The latest flag day, held around the same time, was the best yet.

On Friday 16th June, 1991 the Mayor, Councillor Mary Bradley, launched Hospice Week.

The launch of Hospice Week. Pram-push from the
Guildhall to the site on the Culmore Road.

Chapter Six

The Glorious Opening
The day the tears flowed

Thursday 20th June, 1991

The scene was set. The date for the opening had been picked. Radio Foyle very kindly had agreed to run a live broadcast for one hour during the opening ceremony. Because of the large number attending, it was felt that it could only be held outdoors in the car park area. Even though June can be fine, this was Northern Ireland! The weather could never be guaranteed. On Monday, Tuesday and Wednesday of that week it poured with rain. Then on Thursday 20th, it was sunny and warm all day. People said that Dr McGinley had a direct line to God! Who knows? On the Friday, it rained again!

As the more than four hundred guests gathered and seated themselves in the front of the new hospice, Dr Munro, who was Master of Ceremonies, called everyone to order. Among the speakers were representatives from the Department of the Health and Social Services in Northern Ireland, as well as those from both the Western Health and Social Services and the North Western Health Board in Donegal. The Republic of Ireland's Health Minister, Dr Rory O'Hanlon, spoke, as did the Mayor of Derry, Mary Bradley.

In her address, the Mayor described Thursday June 20th as a momentous day in the life of the city. She said, "The hospice has been provided as a result of the vision and energy of Dr Tom McGinley, who has inspired so many people to take up the challenge to help build the hospice. Derry has shown the world how Christian charity can be practised and I am sure the people of the community will continue to support the facility and its staff and enhance the City's reputation as the most caring community in Ireland." On behalf of the Derry City Council, she extended congratulations to all involved in the hospice.

*Dr Peter Fallon (right) shares one of his many jokes with his partners
Vincent and Tom after the ceremony.*

*Jeremy Harbinson from the DHSS shaking hands with Dr Rory O'Hanlon (centre),
Minister of Health for the Republic of Ireland.*

Dr Jeremy Harbison, representing the Health Minister Jeremy Hanley, said his Department had taken a keen interest in the project and was aware of the hard work which had gone into it, as well as the outstanding support it had received from all sections of the local community.

Dr Rory O'Hanlon, Health Minister in the Republic of Ireland, said he was delighted to be present for the opening of this marvellous facility.

The Chairman of the North Western Health Board, Councillor Noel McGinley, extended congratulations to all involved in the hospice, recalling that it had received tremendous support from the people of Donegal. He described the facility as a 'labour of love' and paid tribute to the energy and leadership of Dr McGinley.

One of the most personal speeches was that of Dr Peter Fallon, Dr Tom's close friend and partner for over thirty years. He saluted those who answered the challenge posed by Dr Tom and ensured his dream would become a reality. He assured them that their efforts would never be forgotten and were deeply appreciated by the medical profession. He paid a special tribute to Dr Tom's wife Deirdre, without whom his friend could not have achieved his dream and vision.

(The following are excerpts taken from the BBC Radio Foyle broadcast of the proceedings. The commentator is Kate O'Halloran)

Kate: Good afternoon and you're welcome to this special edition of the afternoon show. I'm coming to you live from the Foyle Hospice here on the Culmore Road overlooking the River Foyle and dominating the new Foyle Bridge. At this moment what you can hear in the background are the various people representing public bodies who have been involved in the hospice movement getting ready to make their speeches because today is the official opening of the Foyle Hospice for the 400 invited guests.

Dr Keith Munro ...Now – before I introduce the Chairman of the Foyle Hospice to speak to us I myself wish to say a few words about him. Our hospice belongs to the community and it is a community effort that has brought about this success. But if there is one person who needs a special mention, that person is Dr Tom McGinley. It was his vision for the needs of this area that started and stimulated the community effort those many years ago. Those who know him are aware of his extraordinary talents, his tireless energy, his labours day and night year after year, running marathons, organising events, giving lectures, negotiating with statutory bodies, overseeing the homecare service and seeking all the publicity possible for the successful realisation of this vision today. At the same time, he carried on his daily duties as a busy general practitioner and part-time hospital anaesthetist. On many occasions, over the years, I have asked Tom if his everyday work and responsibilities were affected by his involvement in the Foyle Hospice.

He has always been adamant that it didn't. However, he has repeatedly acknowledged that if anyone lost out it, was his wife and family. He has said to me that without their constant support he could not have carried on and we are glad they are here today to see the fruits of those labours. (*Applause*)

Amongst his many talents perhaps his greatest asset has been his ability to motivate people and keep on motivating them. We not only thank the community but all those who gave so freely of their time and effort. We take this opportunity to pay special tribute to Dr Tomás for that vision he had so long ago, the fruits of which now stand before you. I will now call on the Chairman of the Foyle Hospice, Dr Tom McGinley, to speak to us.

Dr Tom McGinley: *A Cháirde*. I would like to welcome you all here on this historic day, on this historic site. When we started looking for a suitable site for a hospice many years ago we always felt that it had to face the bridge and the river. I was brought up in West Donegal on a philosophy that we are all on a journey, and that death is but part of the journey. My thoughts all day have been with that wise lady who introduced me to that philosophy. First of all I would like to thank the Orange Order for selling us this site. (*Applause*).

There is no truth, however, in the fact that I became an honorary member of the Orange Order. (*Laughter*) We are delighted that this programme is going out live on Radio Foyle, and I would like to take the opportunity to thank all those people who can't be here today and who have supported us over the years.

The hospice from day one has highlighted the bridge as our symbol, bridging the gap between life and death. But we were also conscious that unless we built a bridge between our communities we would not be successful. I think very few

Tom with 'the wise woman from West Donegal', his mother, May McGinley. This photo was taken at the time Tom was awarded his Fellowship in Anaesthetics. (1978)

Dr McGinley addresses the guests. (From right in the front row) Dr Peter Fallon, Rev. Ken Best, Bishop Mehaffey, Bishop Daly, Jeremy Harbinson, Mary Bradley (Mayor), Dr Rory O'Hanlon, Noel McGinley, Rev. Maurice Bolton.

View of the river from the Foyle Bridge.

An emotional moment as Dr Tom recieves a standing ovation.

people can deny that we have not bridged that gap. *(Applause)* To those of you listening at home who have supported us financially, I thank you and I'm especially thinking of many, many of you who have given money anonymously. I would also like to thank our committee who have been most supportive but especially two members of that committee, Angela McIntyre and Dr Keith. *(Applause)*.

Many years ago I was visiting a young boy of eighteen who was dying of cancer and I was greatly aware of my inadequacy in looking after him. I am delighted that his sister Briege is here today. I subsequently found out about St Joseph's Hospice in London and over the years I have spent many weeks there. The hospice is run by the Irish Sisters of Charity. I'm delighted that St Joseph's Hospice is represented here today by Sister Joan O'Connor, and I would like publicly to acknowledge the outstanding work they have done in providing end of life care for so many years. There is an old Chinese proverb "better to light a candle than curse the darkness", and I hope that we here in this hospice will continue to carry the candle for those with terminal illness. The debt I owe this community is impossible to put in words. As it draws near to the big moment of the day, and I'm struggling with my emotions, I would like to say that I am very proud, very happy and very, very privileged to be part of this caring community. Thank you. *(Standing ovation)*

Dr Keith Munro: Before we have the ceremony I have a small unscripted part that Tom doesn't know anything about, so he's going to kill me afterwards. I would like to call on Brendan Duddy.

Brendan Duddy: Reverend bishops, ministers, clergy, fellow guests. There have been two women in Tom's life. One, of course, is Deirdre and not enough can be said for what she has put up with. On behalf of this community I would like to thank Deirdre again. *(Applause)* The other woman in Tom's life was his mother and this crystal bridge is not dedicated to Tom but to that woman who was his inspiration. *(Applause)* I now invite Bernie Mount to step forward and present Tom with the crystal bridge specifically designed for this occasion.

Tom with Deirdre, holding the crystal bridge presented in memory of his mother.

Dr Keith Munro: ...So I'll now call on Tom to initiate the ceremony of opening the Foyle Hospice. *(Applause)*

Dr McGinley: We are very honoured today that two children, one a Catholic, one a Protestant, will open this magnificent building. Unfortunately they have one thing in common... When they were only four years of age, they both lost a mother to cancer and we were very, very privileged that our homecare team were involved in caring for their mothers. At this juncture, I would like to emphasize that we will not be looking after everybody with advanced cancer. That care will continue to be done by doctors and nurses in the same way it has always been done. We will provide extra support when needed.

Both mothers died with dignity. Emma and Clare – I will now ask you to walk along to the tape, accompanied by your fathers and followed by the two homecare nurses who were part of the caring team... And as they walk along we should reflect on all the patients who have died in the care of the homecare nurses over the past six years. We have learned so much from them. Perhaps now as they move forward we should all remember those people we have all known, who have died of cancer. *(Pause)*

Clare and Emma then moved forwards together with their fathers Pat McLaughlin and Norman Robinson. They moved towards the tape and together, at three minutes to four, cut the ribbon. There was prolonged and emotional

Clare and Emma prepare to walk forward to officially open the Foyle Hospice.

Clare and Emma both perform the act of cutting the ribbon assisted by Hannah and Rosemary. The girls' fathers, Norman and Pat, are standing behind.

applause. The girls, together with their fathers, Dr McGinley and the two home-care sisters, Hannah and Rosemary, then moved into the building followed by leaders of the four main churches. They were Bishop Daly, Bishop Mehaffey, Rev. Ken Best and Rev. Maurice Bolton.

Then, from inside, came the melodic voices of the choir. The soloists that day were Fidelma Coyle, Anne-Marie Hickey and Tania McGinley. The organ was played by Ruth McGinley. The male soloist was Father Eamon Martin.

The guests then filed slowly into the building to take part in the interdenominational service.

> *"Let them shout for joy, and be glad, that favour my righteous cause: yea, let them say continually, Let the Lord be magnified, which hath pleasure in the prosperity of his servant."* (King James Bible, Psalms)

Representatives of the four main churches leading the celebration service for the official opening of the hospice.(From right) Rev. Maurice Bolton, Bishop Edward Daly, Bishop James Mehaffey and Rev. Kenneth Best.

Excerpts from other interviews recorded after the ceremony by Kate O'Halloran. The first person she interviewed was Sister Joan O'Connor from St Joseph's Hospice in Hackney.

Kate: How did Dr McGinley first get in touch?

Sister Joan: Dr Tom had spent some time at St Joseph's. He wanted to come to experience and learn about hospice philosophy.

A few years ago he then wrote to me about a placement for Rosemary and Hannah who were starting their hospice homecare programme. When I opened his letter and saw the new Foyle Bridge as the logo for the new building my heart missed a beat. Of course, I was delighted and facilitated the two girls. And we are very, very proud of the fact that now a hospice is opening in my own native Derry, the town I love so well. As you know the hospice philosophy is not

Sister Joan O'Connor, who was Matron at St Joseph's Hospice in Hackney, with Dr Tom and Hospice Matron, Rosemary Peoples. This photograph was taken during a visit to Foyle Hospice in 2004.

just helping the patient, so he or she may live fully until they die, but also caring for the family and friends. Death as you all know is the greatest equalizer of all times."

Later Sister Joan told Kate that she had had a sneak look at the hospice before she sat down. "It's only out of this world," she said. "I wish I were working here. This is not a plug but I would come voluntarily. To die in these surroundings would be something different."

The Minister of Health for the Irish Republic Dr Rory O'Hanlon

Kate: Do you think all this could have been possible without the dynamic enthusiasm of Dr Tom McGinley himself?

Minister: No, I've known Tom for a long time and I've always been very impressed by his enthusiasm and particularly his philosophy of caring and his idealism. I believe we can all learn a lot from that, no matter what walk of life we are in. Certainly I believe Tom, with this initiative, has demonstrated his ability as a motivator and has motivated many people. He has cooperated and worked with so many people. I am sure Tom would be the first to say that he couldn't have done it on his own without the support of so many people. He certainly has provided a splendid facility. It is only right that people, who are terminally ill, should have the very best care.

Moderator of the Presbytery of Derry and Strabane
Reverend Maurice Bolton

Kate: Are you impressed with today?

Rev. Bolton: Very impressed! This is a tremendous day, a tremendous day for the whole North-West here. This is one of the finest buildings I have been in. I've been in it earlier when under construction and it is lovely to come back today and see the finished product so well done. Excellent day!

Kate: It was lovely for those looking on to see the four churchmen walking behind the two girls.

Rev. Bolton: Yes, of course, we must remember that the illness which will be treated here, is no respecter of persons. Everybody has their burdens to bear in this way, and if we can't share in such an occasion as this, then there's no hope for mankind. I was delighted today to have the opportunity of being here, especially as Moderator of the Presbytery of Derry and Strabane, here to represent them and take part. I think it's great!

Methodist Church
Reverend Ken Best

Kate: What did you think of the ceremony?

Rev. Best: This has been a marvellous day. Just to be part of this has been very moving in itself; and to see history being made in the care of the terminally ill in Derry. You just feel privileged to be here today.

Kate: Do you think it is significant that the four churches were hand in hand?

Rev. Best: I'm glad we were here because, at the end of things, if we can't show our compassion together then there is something very wrong with our Christianity. So it was lovely that the four church leaders can be here praying together for God to bless this place.

Roman Catholic Bishop of Derry
Dr Edward Daly

Kate: Truly it was a wonderful ceremony wasn't it?

Bishop Daly: It was - absolutely – I thought it was brilliant! The weather, everything! I really thought the whole thing came together. It's tremendous! I think we can be very proud of the city, very proud of the North-West. I think the hospice is something we can all take enormous pride in. Especially, I am so happy for Tom McGinley and for all those associates who have contributed in so many ways over the years. I think this is really a monument of generosity, a monument to caring and a monument to the vision of one particular individual, who saw a need, identified it, and went about realizing it.

Church of Ireland Bishop for Derry & Raphoe
Dr James Mehaffey

Kate: It was a momentous occasion?

Bishop Mehaffey: Yes, I think it was fantastic. First of all, a great tribute must be paid to Dr Tom McGinley and the committee. It was very moving today. Not least the two little girls one Catholic, one Protestant, who cut the tape. Their mothers had died of cancer and yet they were able to stand together, hold the scissors and cut the tape. I think that was marvellously symbolic....the Foyle Hospice took the bridge very much as their symbol. All the work they are doing is bridge-building, between life and death and new life and the provision of hospice services into Donegal. The bridge could be the symbol of all our efforts in church and community.

Grand Master of the City of Derry Grand Orange Lodge
Robert Fleming

Kate: With me now is a very important person in all this scenario – he is Robert Fleming. Robert you're the Grand Master of the City of Londonderry Grand Orange Lodge? It was you who sold them the site?

Robert: Yes – we sold them the site. First of all he only wanted about an acre, then he wanted four acres, then we sold him the whole field.

Kate: So Dr Tom McGinley was greedy, was he?

Robert: No! I think he realized the potentialities of the whole thing and we were willing to facilitate him. We thought the object was for the good of the whole community.

Kate: Of course, now they have the whole site it'll prevent any other development in front of the hospice here?

Robert: Oh! It will. Yes – it will. There will not be any further building on it.

Kate: So did you have a good relationship with this man from west Donegal?

Robert: Oh, we have a very good relationship, very good relationship. We gave him a subscription and presented a painting to the hospice.

Kate: That's right. We were admiring the painting earlier on. When was the first time you saw that Robert?

Robert: The first time I saw it was today. I knew it was coming in, of course.

Kate: What's your opinion of the finished product? Everybody has been admiring it.

Robert: Well – it is very good and very representative of the whole situation as it is at the moment.

Open Day for the Community

After the highly successful opening of the hospice all the people of the North-West and were invited to an Open Day on Saturday 22nd June. The public were then able to see what their generous contributions had created. The day started with a walk from the Waterside over the Foyle Bridge. Personalities from Radio Foyle helped the visitors to have a fun day.

Every year since, an Open Day is organised during June and many events have been staged around the hospice. (See Picture Gallery)

The walk to the hospice for the community on Saturday 22nd June, 1991. It passed over the new Foyle Bridge. (From left) Dean Orr, Rev. Best, Dr Keith Munro, Bishop Mehaffey, Mayor Mary Bradley, Dr Tom McGinley.

In the *Derry Journal* of Friday 21st June, 1991 appeared an extensive article about the opening. These are some extracts:

Derry Doctor's Dream Becomes Reality
MOVING SCENES AS HOSPICE OPENS
by SIOBHAN McELENEY

THE DREAM of a Derry doctor became a reality and the North-West lived up to its reputation as one of the most caring and generous communities in Ireland, with the official opening yesterday of the Foyle Hospice.

Following a moving and highly emotional ceremony, two little Derry girls, Clare McLaughlin and Emma Robinson, one Catholic the other Protestant, who were only four years old when their mothers died of cancer, cut the tape to officially open the facility. Yesterday's ceremony heard that the Hospice would ensure, as its staff had done for the girls' mothers, that the terminally ill would make the final steps in their journey through life with dignity...

It was a proud, historic and indeed joyous day for Derry and the man who inspired the community to become involved in what many regarded as an impossible dream, was overcome with emotion as he addressed the ceremony.

In a very poignant moment one of the Hospices' most loyal supporters who took part in numerous fundraising marathons, Bernie Mount, presented Dr McGinley with a crystal replica of the bridge in memory of his mother. It was a memorable moment in what was one of the most historic and memorable days in Derrys history.

After the inter-denominational service, Siobhan interviewed Bishop Edward Daly who said it was a proud day for the entire community and the magnificent building was a community effort in every sense of the word. A need was identified and a quite inspired effort was made to meet that need. "The fruit of that effort was there for everyone to see," he said. Bishop Daly recalled the origins of the Foyle Hospice and how since then thousands of people of all ages, classess,

religious and political outlooks had been enthusiastically supporting the project. "Jesus Christ taught us to love our neighbour and to care for our neighbour and few neighbours are more in need than the terminally ill and their families," he said. The Bishop expressed sincere thanks, appreciation and congratulations to Dr Tom and all his colleagues, to the nurses and all the caring people involved in the Hospice and those who contributed so generously to the project. "You have served to make this area a more caring and kinder place, this hospice is a monument to your generosity and caring", he stated.

In the *Londonderry Sentinel* of Wednesday 26th June, 1991 there appeared this article:

Foyle Hospice was officially opened on Thursday 20th June, 1991. For all those who were there, this was...

THE DAY THE TEARS FLOWED

Journalists in this city have long been accustomed to learning to cope with their emotions. For many of them, years of murders and subsequent funerals have left them with a hard-hearted attitude to life.

However, last week even the stoniest of hearts would have melted as the new Foyle Hospice was officially opened. The dreams of a local doctor, who bantered and goaded an entire community into giving of their money, was finally realised when the most moving of ceremonies brought about the culmination of his ambition.

As little Clare McLaughlin and Emma Robinson, one Roman Catholic and the other a Protestant, walked forwards to cut the ribbon at the entrance to the impressive building, tears welled in the eyes of all those honoured and indeed privileged to witness the occasion. Clare and Emma, although separated by religion, had one much more important factor bringing them together. Both young ladies lost their mothers to cancer, and as the ribbon fell to the floor one wondered just why people in this country are so insistent on killing their fellow countrymen when diseases such as cancer do the same job so effectively.

The Mayor of the city, Councillor Mary Bradley, and a host of other dignitaries were in attendance. But all will forgive this reporter for not mentioning their attendance any further. This was Tom McGinley's day, it was Derry's day – the day a caring community saw a dream fulfilled.

Yes, this was a day when this particular reporter felt honoured and humbled. I was honoured to have witnessed such a remarkable and memorable achievement and humbled by the dignity of it all and by the sense of occasion.

As one onlooker commented, "Many a time I was down to my last few pounds but when I thought of cancer, I dug deep into my purse and gave them some more money. Were you ever glad you did something?"

Yes, June 20th was that kind of day.

Our Hospice

Like an expectant mother, you await
The arrival of your children.

You look so peaceful and serene,
To sit with you and view God's lovely countryside,
A pleasure to behold.

What a view you command,
The River Foyle gently flows past your door,
The bridge that spans it joining east and west,

Like a long arm extending its welcome,
Though, like a mother, you'll know many tears and sorrows,
The heartaches will be sore.

But through your love and care the rewards you will reap will be many,
Laughter will echo through your home,
Happiness will radiate like the sun.
You see the terminally ill are God's chosen people
And you, the hospice, their saviour.

M.T. (1991)
(The writer had lost her husband to cancer 18 months previously)

For His Dear Friend & Valued Colleague Doctor Tom McGinley,
The closing words of Doctor Peter Fallon's Address, at
The opening of Foyle Hospice, 20ᵗ June 1991.

"When the natural exhultation of this day fades into
the reality of daily life, the doors of this Hallowed
place will welcome its first patients. For them the shadows
will have lengthened, their evening has come, their busy
world has hushed, the fever of life is all but over and
the work is all done.

If they are, in the words of Cardinal Newman,
to achieve a safe lodging, rest, and peace at the last on
this earth, then it will be through the Love and the
Devoted care of the FOYLE HOSPICE, and the
dedicated staff who serve within it."

Dr. Peter Fallon died in the Foyle Hospice on the 25ᵗ of April 1999.
His own devoted life-work for the sick well done, he deeply appreciated the
love & care he received at the Hospice in his last illness.

The above framed picture was later donated by the Fallon family and dedicated to his lifelong friend and valued colleague Dr Tom. It hangs in the front hall of the hospice.

Chapter Seven

Setting up the Inpatient Unit

After she had accumulated six years experience in homecare, Dr McGinley invited Rosemary Peoples to set up the Inpatient Unit. While she carried this out, she continued to work closely with Hannah Walsh in all aspects of homecare.

In October 1991, Rosemary helped a group of ten nurses to settle into the hospice. "We had a very intensive two week induction period for them. Then our first two patients were admitted on 4th November, 1991 which made me excited but apprehensive. We were able to give all our attention to Lily Harris and Betty Hamill. Lily died on Christmas Eve. This was the first big jolt for us all. The reality of life in the hospice struck home. All staff hoped that both these ladies would enjoy Christmas together. Betty did live into the New Year, however, listening to the songs of Daniel O'Donnell that she loved so much. She then died peacefully on 13th January, 1992.

"While the vast majority of patients were admitted for terminal care, some came for respite. As well as those suffering from cancer, other patients with non-malignant conditions were admitted for pain control, as were those suffering from motor neurone disease. Staff slowly got used to the specialised nursing required for end-of-life care. All of them had come from different disciplines and had to get used to the pace of life in the hospice which was much slower. Time was needed for all staff to bond together."

Then the post of Matron was advertised. Rosemary said, "I always intended to go back to homecare. I was very happy there. However family and friends persuaded me to apply. I had nothing to lose. I was delighted when I was appointed. I realised I was finally leaving homecare for good."

She describes how wonderful the working environment was for patients and staff alike. "The front hall of the hospice is great and emphasises the fact that this is not a hospital. There is no restriction on visiting. Patients, as well as relatives, can watch the horses in the field. Sometimes they see young foals galloping around or look out at the beautiful flowers, like daffodils in spring.

Nuala Kelly, nursing officer of the City Red Cross, presents a cheque for £3,000 to purchase a specialised bed for the hospice to Dr Tom McGinley. (From left) Rosie Green and Theresa McSwiney, Mr Ronnie Harvey, FRCS, Medical Officer, City Red Cross, and Rosemary Peoples. Mr Harvey was also a Trustee of the Hospice. (10th Dec, 1991)

Young foals often seen from the hospice

"They have a clear view of the bridge, which helps staff to explain the symbolism of the hospice. When possible, we let patients do any special things they may have longed to do. I remember Bishop Daly taking a man out who used to work on the railways. He took him on the train at the railway museum. On occasion, patients would be amazed to see Dr McGinley working the gardens late on a summer's evening. He would often have a chat through the open window.

"Staff themselves would fundraise, such as helping with the Christmas bazaar. Relatives would bring cakes and buns. At first we had a Christmas tree in the front hall. Later we started the very popular 'switching on the Christmas lights' in the grounds of the hospice. Relatives and friends bought a light in memory of a loved one.

"Every death in the hospice is very sad and upsetting for all of us, as well as the relatives and friends of course. It was particularly hard for me when one particular lady died. That was Majella Donaghy, who had been a friend of mine at school and had worked so hard for the Top of the Hill Hospice Support Group.

"We try to keep life as normal as possible. All birthdays are celebrated, staff share bits of their own lives, and there is always lots of laughter. Patients are often amazed when they arrive, especially when coming from an acute hospital. One particular patient was astonished to be allowed a long lingering bath. They would say things like, 'It's heaven'; 'it's like a hotel'; 'it's not like a hospital', and even, 'How could you not be happy here?'"

Doreen Guy with Dr Tom switching on the Christmas lights in 2002. Her husband, Jim, a Trustee of Foyle Hospice and former Mayor of the City, had died earlier that year.

The Christmas lights switched on after the carol service in 2004.

A choir from Oakgrove Integrated Primary School singing carols around the tree in 2004.

Warm and welcoming front hall of the hospice.

The beautiful fireplace in the front hall.

The 'Book of Remembrance' has a page for each day of the year. The name of every person who has died in the hospice is recorded on the specific day.

One of the many beautiful paintings presented to the hospice over the years adorns the walls. This view of Mount Errigal was presented in memory of Kate McKeever, of Hamilton Street, by her son John.

Early Memories of Inpatient Nursing

Teresa McGowan – day staff

"I remember standing in the front hall of the Foyle Hospice for the first group photograph of nurses for the newly-opened hospice. We were a diverse and enthusiastic group with different personalities, nursing backgrounds and experiences. What we had in common was a genuine desire and commitment to nursing cancer patients and to do whatever we could to support them and their families through what was a very traumatic period in their lives.

"While being experienced nurses, we soon learned that we had a lot more to learn about palliative/terminal care and, thanks to Dr McGinley, our education soon began. He taught us about pain pathways and neurotransmitters, intrathecal blocks etc. etc. All this was new language for us. Day after day, he persisted in explaining, encouraging and empowering us to become more skilled and knowledgeable in symptom control with special emphasis on the relief of pain. Through his personality and extensive experience, he moulded this enthusiastic and diverse nursing group into a very professional and specialist palliative care

Matron with Dr McGinley, in light-hearted mood with nurses. (From left) Rosemary Peoples, Dr McGinley, Kathleen Dunne, Donna Semple, Rachel Kenny, a visiting nurse from University of Ulster, Lucy Armstrong, Annette Gamble.

Enjoying a wee drink

nursing team. His anaesthetic training was invaluable. We took a pride in ensuring patients were pain free.

"My personal knowledge of drugs was greatly enhanced. What was innovative in the Foyle Hospice nearly 14 years ago is now standard practice in palliative care centres.

"The hospice was more than about high quality nursing care. It was also about humour and personalised attention. Patients who enjoyed a 'wee drink' led to the introduction of a night-cap for those who wanted it. Some patients requested ice lollipops and this led to every patient having their own fridge. Bishop Daly would secretly leave sweets in patients' lockers so that their children would find them while visiting.

"I was proud to be part of the early days of the Foyle Hospice. I have worked with many good and caring people such as Dr McGinley, Bishop Daly and my nursing colleagues. More significantly, I have met, and got to know people who have shown great humanity and dignity in the face of sadness and adversity. I will always be grateful for that experience as a nurse and a human being."

Monica Cunningham and Yvonne Martin – night duty

"All the newly appointed nurses were given an intensive two week induction period under the direction of Dr McGinley and the homecare team consisting of Hannah Walsh and Rosemary Houston. We all had good basic nursing skills. These, coupled with enthusiasm, went a long way to providing the care that our patients and their families needed so much in the final weeks and days of life. Topics covered during these two weeks included pain control, management of nausea and vomiting, management of breathlessness, and communication skills. These were invaluable to us all, as none of us had specific specialist palliative care experience. Education was by formal lectures and case studies. Role play was also initiated, which added to a greater depth of understanding of the special needs of people with advanced cancer. Some of the handouts distributed at this stage are still vital tools used by nurses up to this present day. All staff were updated regularly over subsequent years with developments in specialist palliative care. This included all aspects of care, from symptom management to ensuring that families and carers' needs were addressed at all stages of the illness.

"At 9.45pm on 4th November,1991 the 'crème de la crème' of new staff walked through the front door of the Inpatient Unit to start the ten hour shift. Our enthusiasm took over and our fears soon subsided as we got on with the job in hand. At last we were providing palliative care to the first patients admitted to the hospice earlier that day. Coming from a hospital background with medical backup at the end of a 'bleep', now we were faced with the responsibility of patients, in unfamiliar territory to us all. Unknown to us, help was nearer to hand than we realised. During the medicine round, which took a lot of concentration due to the giving of controlled drugs, we suddenly heard the jingle of keys behind us. Turning round we saw Dr McGinley at our heels. He had quietly entered the building by the back door and crept up the corridor. After surviving the shock of his presence right beside us, we were always glad to see him as he was able to clarify queries we had regarding patient care. Naturally the patients just loved to see him coming! Due to our lack of experience in palliative care during those early weeks, his direction and support was much appreciated. However, there was a downside. Dr McGinley was always asking us questions relating to drugs, pain pathways, vomiting reflex pathways, nerve supply to this and that, and so on. The list went on and on and on. Sometimes we were fortunate enough to get a tip-off from the day staff indicating his pet topic of the day. Time permitting, there was a flurry of activity to the text books in order to digest knowledge on that topic prior to his nightly visit. However, too much knowledge couldn't be divulged as this meant even deeper probing until, eventually, we got so confused and mixed up that we nearly got our knickers in a twist!

"In the early days of the hospice there were a lot of fears and misconceptions that 'patients didn't come out of there again', and that 'you go there to die'. Our memories of night duty showed us that in fact the reverse was true and that the care provided was total. This was demonstrated in the active medical intervention initiated by Dr McGinley, much of it stemming from his anaesthetic expertise. Some of the interventions initiated included the management of epidural infusions, nerve blocks and ketamine and lignocaine infusions. This active treatment helped change beliefs and misconceptions about the hospice. Patients received the appropriate care needed to keep them comfortable and pain free. This allowed them the best quality of life possible.

The Duchess of Norfolk with staff during her visit to the hospice. (1992) Yvonne is third from the left (front). Monica is the blonde at the back.

"Close relationships were fostered with patients and families, particularly so on night-duty. There was less 'hustle and bustle' than often found on day-duty, leaving quality time for staff to sit and talk to patients.

"Fourteen years on we are still fondly remembered and gratefully acknowledged as the 'wee nurse' who looked after 'my husband', 'my father', or 'my mother'. Being acknowledged like this makes us realise that it's all worthwhile.

"As time went by our skills and confidence developed within each of us. Dr McGinley's visits at night became fewer. His confidence in our own ability had obviously increased. All his teaching was working. Finally we were left with the responsibility for the Inpatient Unit, but instructed by Dr McGinley to 'ring me at home if you need me'. Many an early morning, this left us with a dilemma. Do we, or do we not, ring him about a change in a patient's condition at 6am? Questions would be asked. 'Do you think he'd be up yet for his early morning run?', 'What if he's in the shower and we wake Deirdre?', 'Will we ring, or should we wait another half and hour?'

"The decision would finally be made. 'We'd better ring now or he'll wonder why we took so long, especially if the change had occurred an hour-and-a-half ago!'

"Despite all our fears and anxieties about those early night-duty months, we had good 'craic' with patients, families and our colleagues. Some nights we had to change our role from nurse to chef! Steroid therapy, started for symptom

"CHEERS!"

Julie McColgan, a young lady from Newtownstewart, was admitted for assessment and treatment of her non-malignant condition. Her artistic talents were displayed when she penned this humorous caricature of Dr Tom. She was made aware by staff of his lifelong abstention from tobacco, alcohol and his dislike of spectacles. This is even funnier when one knows of his great pride in dress, and his insistence on 'sartorial elegance'! He was presented with this cartoon after returning from his usual weekend in Gweedore. Julie remains in reasonably good health. She now has a flat of her own. The few weeks she spent in the hospice helped her greatly to learn to live with her pain.

management, had minor drawbacks. One of the side-effects was suffering from pangs of hunger in the middle of the night, resulting in requests for different foods. A nurse would don a chef's cap and rustle up an omelette and chips at 2am! Once the patient's hunger was satisfied, it was vital the kitchen was left clean and tidy or else we had to deal with Ena's wrath! Naturally the kitchen was her pride and joy – not to mention she had red hair! After all, it must be remembered that we provided active, total care to our patients and, if that meant cooking a meal in the middle of the night, so be it."

Monica joined the homecare team in June, 1999. Yvonne became a Foyle Hospice homecare nurse in Inishowen in June, 1997. She is now employed by the North-Western Health Board in that role. Both feel that it was an honour and a privilege to have been part of the original nursing team.

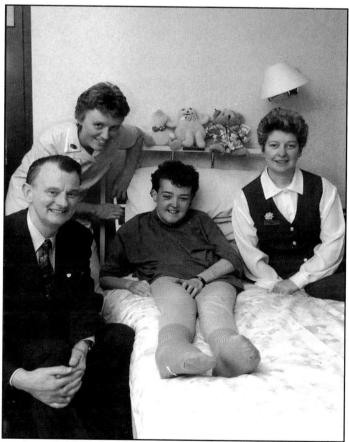

Lena Carney from Foxford, Co. Mayo. She had worked as a nanny in London. After her diagnosis of cancer, she requested to be cared for in Foyle Hospice for the terminal stage of her disease. She died in the hospice on 8th May, 1994. Nancy Moran (behind Dr Tom) is now a homecare sister in Sligo.

Dr Tom McGinley pictured in Nov 1994 with (from left) Evelyn McCaffrey, Lena O'Reilly, Rosemary Peoples; Annette Gamble, (nursing staff), and Bridget Morrison.

Young Emmett Canning who was an inpatient for one week in November 1996. Seen here with Teresa and Hannah and Eileen Jennings. Emmett died at home one week after his discharge.

Normal life goes on. Ladies come to play bridge with patients. (1996)

Hazel Kelly in a light-hearted moment with Dr Tom in the Inpatient Unit. She was in charge of the nurses' home in St Columb's Hospital. She died in the hospice in 2000.

Mina Pollock about to blow out the candles on her birthday cake. She had managed the well known Sidebottom's fish shop in Carlisle Road for many years, where Dr McGinley had been a frequent visitor! This picture was taken a few weeks prior to her death in the hospice in April 2001.

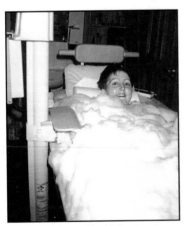

The bliss of bubbles in the popular jacuzzi.

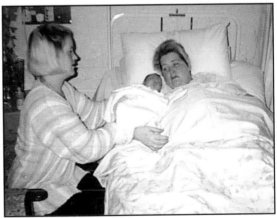

Happy to see a new grandchild.

Charlie Duffy enjoying a visit from Norman Wisdom and other celebrities who had been participating in a Golf Classic to raise funds for the hospice. Charlie was very well known to staff as he had been admitted on numerous occasions for respite care.

Ena Quigley looks happy in the arms of Norman Wisdom.

Cooks and Catering

Catering is so vitally important in any hospice. Although kitchen staff are not dealing with large numbers it is essential to meet the requirements of all the individual patients, some of whom will have little or no appetite. "Ena Quigley has been the head cook since the opening of the hospice," says Terri Sythes. "Unfortunately she has moved recently to other employment. She was ably assisted by June Callan, Helen Dunwoody, Jim Doherty and Kay Stewart. Helen moved to Daycare after it opened." Ann Scott joined the hospice staff as head cook in August 2005.

Ena Quigley, with Jim Doherty.

June Callan.

Kay Stewart, Catering Assistant.

Volunteers

"Some of the most important people, providing a vital service for the hospice, are the volunteers," says Terri speaking glowingly and with pride.

"We have some 50 regular volunteers who serve in various capacities. We always get more applications than available posts. Some of them have been with us since the very beginning. They do so many things such as flower arranging, kitchen duties, daycare, maintenance, cleaning, laundry and fundraising. Their invaluable services are a major financial saving for the hospice."

One of the very early volunteers was Mary McDaid. Dr Tom persuaded her to become involved in fundraising very early in the 1980s.

Mary says, "My good friend Bridie Glenn also became involved at that time. We organised raffles, and local business people were most generous. When the Weekly Draw started, Bridie and I became promoters. A friendly rivalry developed between us to see who got the most members for the draw. Shortly after the hospice opened, I became a volunteer and started to help in the kitchen and with flower arranging. I subsequently became a member of the 'Forget-Me-Not' bereavement group along with Evelina Gallagher and Eamon Duffy. I am very much involved with the hospice choir, along with George Kelkie. Sunday Mass is very much appreciated by patients and their families, and Bishop Daly makes the Mass so special." Mary looks back over all those years, "To be involved with the hospice is so fulfilling, and it has changed my outlook in many ways. My life is much richer for sharing the final journey with our patients. I feel very privileged to be part of the hospice family."

Mary McDaid in one of her many roles.

Teresa Bryce helped out in the laundry. She died in the hospice on 2nd July, 2000

Early Partners in Administration

Bernadette Healy / Terri Sythes

Two members of the early 'Admin Team' were Bernadette Healy and Terri Sythes. 'Come to Derry, free travel, free accommodation and raise some money for Foyle Hospice.' This was the first mention of Foyle Hospice for Terri. "I had arrived at the RDS in Dublin to register for the 1984 Women's Mini Marathon. I was tempted at first by the offer of a free weekend in Derry, but being a 'street-wise Dub', I decided there must be a catch. I passed up the opportunity. Little did I know, a couple of years later, I would be sitting nervously in 9 Crawford Square waiting for an interview for a job on the ACE Scheme – Action for Community Employment."

Both Terri and Bernadette were interviewed for ACE jobs during March 1987.

Bernadette's journey to ACE, however, was slightly different. "While paying a visit to Derry in early summer of 1984, my sisters-in-law complained to me about the training schedule inflicted upon them each week in the grounds of Templemore Sports Complex by a certain Dr Tom McGinley. They explained that they were participating in the first Foyle Hospice Female Run. It couldn't have been too bad. They all looked forward immensely to the training and successfully completed the run. I might add, they have taken part in subsequent walks, with their daughters, every year since. I had no idea at that time what a hospice was! Little did I know then that less than three years later I would be working for that self-same charity in their office at 9 Crawford Square."

Apart from Bernadette and Terri, three other ACE workers were employed, Mary Doherty, Kieran and Mary Gill. Bernadette still did not know what a hospice was. "I learned quite a lot in those early days. When things were quiet in the office I used to read books from the hospice library and learned about the importance of the new service being provided."

Terri Sythes with Dr Tom and Deirdre (February 2002).

Terri describes the early days in Crawford Square. "There was a constant stream of people calling to pay in their weekly draw money, looking for bargains in the shop or just making donations.

"I was quite in awe of Dr McGinley, and while I was counting copper hunt money he often stopped to help. This made me nervous, and I constantly seemed to knock over the money he had just counted!

"One of the many regulars who called was Len Ball, who organised the annual Christmas Day swim in memory of his son Liam. It is now organised by his daughter Kathleen (his grand-daughter Cathy is one of our nursing staff). During this time, the first car draw took place and for weeks it was impossible to walk around the office because of the hundreds of books of tickets piled everywhere. Everyone who called in was handed a book of tickets. We thought we were doing well until we realised that for every book we distributed Dr McGinley had taken at least ten. This was a nightmare for our record keeping. However he had his own 'inbuilt' computer and knew exactly the number of books he had taken."

Bernadette's year ended all too soon. ACE workers have to leave after a year. "However," says Bernadette, "one year later, I was then eligible for another ACE post and returned to work again at Crawford Square in June 1989. By then things had changed. There were now more employees, more members in the weekly draw, and an increase in donations. The Copper Hunt, was now in full swing.

Terri recollects other conscientious workers in those days. "In 1994, Eileen Hasson, an ACE worker, began working in Crawford Square. From day one, Eileen was really interested in the hospice and in fundraising. When she applied for a permanent job she was successful. After it was decided to build the Fundraising Centre on the Culmore Road, Eileen was really excited and looked forward so much to moving into the new offices. Sadly, she took ill and died in the hospice in October 2000. It was ironic that both Alistair Kinkaid and Eileen Hasson, who worked together in Crawford Square, died in the hospice. Both of them are still sadly missed."

At the end of Bernadette's second year, she was awarded a permanent post. "There was great excitement in 1991 when the new Inpatient Unit was officially opened in June," she continues. "I was on maternity leave at the time and had been advised by my GP to bed rest but I wasn't going to miss the grand opening! In 1992, we decided to centralise the administration service and I moved down to the new unit to work with Terri. Crawford Square continued to be the Fundraising Centre. The beautiful surroundings of the unit were a welcome change."

Terri speaks of those exciting times in the new administrative surroundings in the Inpatient Unit. "It was a great time to work here and a real learning curve for us all, as everything was new. The building had to be fitted out, suppliers found, volunteers contacted. I had never worked in a healthcare setting before. One day, I was handed a list of names and telephone numbers with the heading 'BANK'. Never having heard of the system of bank nurses, I assumed I was to ring and find out details of their bank accounts! Initially I worked at reception, but over the years my role developed. I am now the Administrative Services Manager looking after the administration, catering and cleaning departments as well as all the volunteers. We have two full-time cleaners in the Inpatient Unit. Gary Rudd joined us in January1994 and Carol McGurk in July, 2001. Geraldine Hegarty cleans the Daycare and Fundraising Centres, and joined the team in March 2004. Between them they keep the Foyle Hospice complex spotless."

Likewise Bernadette's work has changed as well. "Today, the administration and fundraising activities of the hospice have grown so much that we now have fourteen employed in those areas. We have more than one hundred employees in total. My own role has changed, and now my main responsibilities are accounting and payroll. I have been associated with Foyle Hospice since the early days, and I have witnessed its development and role within the community's social history."

These sentiments are echoed by Terri, who started on the same day so many years ago. "I feel very privileged to work at Foyle Hospice, and I have learned so much from my involvement and have made many good friends. It is wonderful to know that, in some small way, I am helping people. Our hospice is a very important part of my life."

Andrena Arbuckle joined the office team at the Inpatient Unit on 23rd November, 1998, having come from working in a solicitor's office. She is the welcoming face for visitors and guests and has responsibility for all donations. Her secretarial skills are invaluable to Dr Tom. She jokingly calls him a 'fusspot' because of his absolute obsession with every little detail.

Subsequently Bernadette Wilkinson, 'the quiet one', joined on 18th April, 2001. She has specific responsibility for gift aided donations and assists in many other varied administrative duties. She deputizes for Andrena when she is on leave. Her husband, Colm, who was involved in many fundraising events for the hospice, sadly died in January, 2000.

After the first patients were admitted in November 1991, the day-to-day medical cover was provided by a number of doctors, on a part-time basis, including Dr Tom Black, Dr Michelle Stone, Dr Nicola Herron and Dr Noel

Bernadette Healy and Bernadette Wilkinson consulting in the office.

Andrena's welcoming smile.

Boyle. While Tom continued to work full time in his practice, and carry out his anaesthetic sessions in Altnagelvin Hospital, he was also the specialist in charge of the patients in the hospice. As soon as he went part-time in Aberfoyle, he was able to increase his work at the hospice. In 1995, he retired from anaesthetic work and, in 1997, from his general practice. This was the year after the retirement of his long-time partner and friend Dr Peter Fallon. Tom was now able to devote all his time to medical and administrative work in the hospice.

The medical cover for nights and weekends from the opening of the hospice was provided by Tom's colleagues in Aberfoyle.

Dr Vincent Cavanagh takes up the story:

> "This was done willingly for many years. Tom has always acknowledged the major financial savings for the hospice. Our initial involvement was undertaken with a certain amount of apprehension as we

were not so familiar with the techniques of syringe drivers, equivalent drug doses, and the changing of one treatment regime to another. We soon came to realise that most patients were stabilised on treatment before we even saw them. We learned to accept and greatly value the very experienced advice of the skilled hospice nursing staff. Tom had seen to it that they were well qualified, as well as comprehensively trained by himself. The Aberfoyle admin staff have also shown great enthusiasm by giving their time to becoming involved in all sorts of fundraising events, and this has continued through the years up to the present day.

"Looking back, we provided a very comprehensive terminal care service at Aberfoyle. We discussed our terminal patients on an ongoing daily basis with each other as well as with our marvellous district nurses. We liaised with Marie Curie nurses on a regular basis. Each doctor tried to look after his own cases, as far as possible. Visiting patients, when not on call at nights or weekends, gave us the opportunity to spend valuable time with our ill patients without the constant problems of being interrupted by other emergency calls. It also allowed time for discussion with other family members. Our work was constrained, however, by the limited nature of the drugs available in the early days and by the different approach to terminal care by medical science and popular opinion. We tried to compensate by working the long hours, anticipating medical and social problems. A great deal of help was given directly, by talking as honestly as possible. Families coped amazingly well with unfamiliar and serious difficulties. The clergy showed themselves to be strong and prayerful servants of the people. It goes without saying that we all worked in the areas of anxiety, depression and bereavement.

"There are many people who have contributed to the work of the hospice over all these years. What continues to inspire is my knowledge that many have had to cope with problems of illness themselves and in their families.

"The relief, over the years, to so many families is beyond measure. The support from all sides of the community speaks for itself and must be almost unique. We are indeed blessed to have such a place of dedicated care and practical skill, and it is the combining of these two essential works which create such a blessing."

Chapter Eight

Hands across the Border

From the moment the hospice was launched, Dr Tom was determined that services would extend throughout Donegal. During his years as a GP he had patients on both sides of the border and felt strongly that geographical boundaries should not exclude patients with advanced cancer from access to specialist services. Once Hannah and Rosemary had been established in homecare, Tom addressed various groups of GPs in Donegal and explained the services available for their patients, if they wished. Hannah and Rosemary travelled to many parts of Donegal, including as far as Ballyshannon and Dungloe.

Then, an event occurred which was, according to Dr Tom, the catalyst and inspiration for the hospice in Donegal. Dr James McDaid takes up the story, in the Donegal Hospice Newsletter of September 1999.

"Little Adrian Mitchell was six years old and suffering from a kidney tumour with multiple bone secondaries. He was in agonizing pain. To ease this, I was giving him pethidine and morphine. I will always remember how he had to steel himself for the injections which, very understandably for a young lad, he dreaded. Yet he knew that without the injection he would suffer unbearably. I remember that we got in touch with the Foyle Hospice in Derry, which provided a syringe driver. This eliminated the need for repeated injections. Seeing how Foyle Hospice was able to help us, in that situation, by alleviating Adrian's suffering, Dr Tom McGinley and I, and other helpers, made up our minds that we would have to establish a hospice in Donegal. Little Adrian died, pain free, shortly after."

Dr McDaid, along with Dr Ann Doherty, Geraldine McIntyre and others formed the committee which became the Donegal Hospice Group. In March 1989, after Helen McMahon was appointed, they arranged a major meeting to officially launch the Donegal Hospice Homecare services.

The first major cross-border cheque donation received from Sister Mercedes, Matron of Dungloe District Hospital, West Donegal. This £2,500 was presented, proceeds from a garden fete held during 1988. (Back left) Rosemary, Hannah, (Foyle Hospice Homecare), Nurses Flor McBride and Mardi Boyd from the Dungloe District Hospital.

Helen McMahon takes up the story:

"I was employed as a Macmillan Sister in south London in 1988, when I first became aware of the position of Homecare Sister in County Donegal. Immediately prior to that, I had worked as a staff nurse at Trinity Hospice in Clapham, London, having completed the ENB 931 course in the Care of the Dying run jointly between Trinity and St Joseph's Hospice in Hackney. I was appointed in January 1989 by the Foyle Hospice, and was assigned the task of establishing the new palliative care service in County Donegal under the direction of Dr Tom McGinley, Medical Director.

"From the outset, I was made extremely welcome and every effort was made to facilitate my work and the service being provided. I knew from prior experience that this was not always the case, and that the introduction of palliative care services was often greeted with suspicion

(Back row) Arthur Sheffield (Cancer Relief Macmillan Fund), Rosemary and Hannah (Foyle Hospice Homecare), Tom Hudson, Chief Executive of the Irish Cancer Society, Dr Peter Fallon (Derry GP), Gretta (Foyle Hospice Homecare) and Helen McMahon (Donegal Hospice Homecare). (Front row) Dr Seán O'Sullivan (Donegal GP), Dr Tom, Rory O'Hanlon (Minister of Health for the Republic of Ireland), Dr James McDaid (Donegal GP), Vincent Kozell (Chairman of Daffodil Fund Committee, Irish Cancer Society), Donal O'Shea, (Chief Executive of the Northern Health Board).

This photograph was taken when the Donegal Hospice Homecare was officially launched at the Mount Errigal Hotel in Letterkenny, in March 1989. This venture was a unique example between not only the statutory and voluntary bodies involved, but also between agencies on either side of the border. Helen was to be employed by Foyle Hospice in Derry, funded by the Irish Cancer Society in Dublin, with additional funding from the Donegal Hospice, to provide a hospice service for the North Western Health Board in Donegal.

and even resentment by established health care professionals. This is understandable when one considers the reality that care has long been delivered by experienced doctors and nurses, to all patients in need, including those with advanced cancer and other life-threatening illnesses. The advent of such a new specialised service, if not introduced with sensitivity and in a spirit of cooperation, runs the risk of marginalizing and deskilling the very professionals who carry the prime responsibility of caring for these patients and their families.

"Soon after I was appointed, I encountered an example of resentment among community nurses in the south of Ireland. Dr McGinley and I were invited to speak at a meeting organised by Tom Hudson, Chief Executive of the Irish Cancer Society. The meeting had been arranged in an attempt to overcome a degree of resistance to the proposed introduction of a palliative care service in the North- East. This had become apparent during the efforts of the Irish Cancer Society to garner local support for the appointment of a specialist homecare nurse and seemed to be based upon a mistaken concept of that nurse's role. Dr McGinley and I enthusiastically, yet diplomatically, presented our role and experiences to the assembled group, which included a number of Public Health nurses. I expected a certain amount of scepticism and suspicion, based upon prior experience in London, but nothing prepared me for the hostility with which our presentation was received. The prevailing feeling was perhaps best summarised in the words of one stern nurse, who gravely pronounced that the day on which she needed advice from anyone on the matter of patient care, was the day that she would resign. I vividly recall my sense of discomfiture, to the extent that I felt constrained to admit to all and sundry that I was very glad that a strong, wide desk separated them from me!

"For the first year, I was responsible for establishing and delivering a palliative care service within Letterkenny General Hospital and most of the County Donegal area, and I was based in the hospital itself. In those early days, no specialist hospice beds were available, until the Foyle Hospice Inpatient unit was opened in 1991. Much of that early time was spent in education, particularly for the public, in order to heighten awareness of the service and to explain what could be offered to patients and their families. The first step was to introduce myself and the service by writing to and meeting all of the GPs within the area.

"I also met hospital consultants and staff. I was invited to speak to various professional groups, especially acute and community hospital/nursing unit managers and staff, and public health nurses. Invitations to speak were also accepted from various church groups and fundraising events.

"The level of interest and support which I encountered was almost overwhelming. However, there is a certain stigma attached to the work of hospice and pain management, and that support and appreciation for what was being provided was also tinged with fear and anxiety. One of the greatest challenges at that time, which unfortunately persists to an extent to this day, was to try to alter the dominant negative image of palliative care and its powerful association

Derry-Donegal Hospice Linkup. Minister of Health Rory O'Hanlon congratulating newly appointed Donegal hospice homecare nurse Helen McMahon. He was attending a meeting arranged in the Mount Errigal Hotel in Letterkenny and entitled, 'A Model of Care for the Terminally Ill in Donegal'. Also present Dr James McDaid, Chairman of the Donegal Hospice Group. (March 1989)

with inappropriate opioid use and imminent death. One way to overcome this perception was to encourage referral at an earlier point in the patient's illness rather than waiting until they were *in extremis*. Sadly, fear and ignorance, on the part both of families and professionals, can still lead to patients suffering needlessly for weeks, months and even years, because it is imagined that agreeing to the visit of the specialist palliative care nurse will lead directly and swiftly to deterioration and death. Deferred requests to visit patients only during their last days or hours merely serve to perpetuate this destructive myth. A much-dreaded stranger is invited to the home, at a time of enormous distress and grief, and is unrealistically expected to resolve complex problems within hours of arrival. Fortunately this is now a much rarer scenario, but is by no means unknown.

"Referrals were accepted from hospital consultants and general practitioners, and it was made clear from the outset that no patient would be visited without the permission of the responsible medical clinician. This was to be no more than a complementary service, supplementing the care which had long been delivered by doctors and nurses without expert help. It would provide a resource for specialist skills and knowledge relating to symptom control and family support, offering advice and monitoring where appropriate. Suggestions regarding management would be given, but the ultimate decision concerning prescribing would always by made by the physician with clinical responsibility. A central tenet of palliative care philosophy has always been to share care and to increase the skills and knowledge of all individuals involved, both professional and lay, including the patient her/himself.

"The service was in many ways a model of cooperative, integrated care. In my capacity as palliative care nurse within the acute hospital, I was in the fortunate position of being able to meet most patients prior to their discharge. Symptom control, rapport and trust could be achieved during their hospital stay, and this could then be continued following their discharge home. The service continued to expand over the years to the level it has achieved today."

Some months after the official launch, the various agencies involved arranged a follow-up meeting. This included Dr Tom McGinley (Foyle Hospice), Dr James McDaid (Donegal Hospice), Tom Hudson (Chief Executive of the Irish Cancer Society), and Manus Ward (North Western Health Board in Donegal).

The main aim of this meeting was to plan for the provision of all necessary care for those with advanced cancer and, in addition, support for family and friends. It was highlighted that success depended on a close relationship between the voluntary and statutory bodies. The emphasis was to be on the development of homecare, with inpatient services being provided within existing Health Board Hospitals in close liaison with Foyle Hospice. It was decided that regular meetings between the various groups would take place to monitor the progress of this agreement.

Manus Ward said that his Board was considering Dr McGinley's suggestion that they appoint a trained nurse in terminal care for the Letterkenny Hospital. She would have overall responsibility within the hospital for terminally ill patients and their families. This nurse would work in close liaison with the homecare sisters. He went on to say that discussions were progressing with regard to the setting up a symptom control team within the hospital. The Board was also committed to an ongoing educational programme. Such a programme was currently in an advanced stage of planning, in conjunction with Foyle

Hospice, and the initial part of this programme would start with a two-day course for nurses in Letterkenny in October 1989. Nurses from the Donegal region would also be able to avail of ongoing educational programmes at Foyle Hospice.

Dr McDaid stressed that there were no plans for a separate hospice Inpatient Unit in Donegal at present. Their funds, initially, were to provide for a homecare sister. This funding has now largely been taken over by the Irish Cancer Society. Funds would now be directed towards educating nurses and other medical personnel as well as providing practical aids and help in the home environment.

Any shortfall in Helen McMahon's funding would be absorbed by their group. He added that they were very pleased with the cooperation between the various voluntary and statutory bodies.

Tom Hudson was delighted at the success of the cooperation. "This is a model," he said, "being studied closely by other health boards in Ireland. Our society is also committed to ongoing education, and we're delighted at the workshops being planned by the North Western Health Board and Foyle Hospice. There is a lot of interest being shown in these in other parts of the country. Overall we are especially delighted at the cross-border initiative being shown by Dr McGinley and Foyle Hospice."

Dr McGinley congratulated the North Western Health Board in Donegal on their cooperation and positive action. "They have accorded a very high priority in the development of these services in their area and have responded very positively by creating specific appointments and a firm commitment to the training of existing staff." He thanked the Irish Cancer Society for their funding and their commitment to education and also the Donegal hospice group who had achieved so much in such a short time.

Tom continued to work closely with Donal O'Shea, Chief Executive of the North Western Health Board in Donegal and with Manus Ward. They were of the opinion that eventually a hospice would be required in Letterkenny for the Donegal area, if money became available from their Department of Health. However, in the meantime, the hospice homecare programme needed to be developed. It was felt that due to Inishowen being the natural hinterland of Derry, homecare in that area would be covered by Foyle Hospice. He and Donal concluded that one or two rooms in each district hospital should, ideally, be set aside for terminal care patients. These districts hospitals included ones in Donegal Town, Dungloe, Falcarragh and Carndonagh. The programme manager for hospitals in the North Western Health Board, Manus Ward, was to become heavily involved in these plans. In 1990, the North Western Health Board appointed a second homecare nurse, Sr. Magdalene Moore, who had gained experience in this field in the United States. She and Helen worked closely and agreed to divide the region between them into two separate areas of responsibility. Sr. Magdalene was based in Donegal Town, covering the south and west of the county, whilst Helen remained in Letterkenny covering most of the north and east. Foyle Hospice was to continue cover of the Inishowen peninsula.

Dr McGinley was the overall Medical Director of Hospice Services for both Foyle and Donegal. He continued to hold meetings with GPs and nurses, on a regular basis, throughout the county. This included participating in ongoing educational programmes organised by the Irish Cancer Society, in which Helen McMahon was also involved. Once the Inpatient Unit was opened in Foyle (1991), patients from many parts of Donegal were admitted for symptom control as well as terminal care. Both the North Western Health Board and the Donegal Hospice Group contributed to the funding for these patients until Donegal acquired its own Inpatient Unit.

On 19th March, 1991 Ann Nash from Bath, England, gave a workshop on palliative care at the Foyle Hospice, Crawford Square. Dr Tom and Helen McMahon (Donegal Homecare) are either side. Fifty nurses gathered from many parts of Ireland. They were all involved in hospice care. (Back row from left) Gretta Linehan, Angela McIntyre, Rosemary and Hannah, with Sister Magdalene (Donegal Homecare).

Theresa McSwiney – memories of homecare nursing in Inishowen

"My career at Foyle Hospice started in October 1991 when the Inpatient Unit opened. I worked as a staff nurse in the unit for about a year. I then re-located to homecare. The team consisted of Hannah Healy and myself, and eventually Mandy Bradley joined us. Hannah and I started up the first daycare service, which was rather slow to take-off. We persisted, however, together with Mandy Bradley, Kathleen Boyle and many volunteers. We provided relaxation and fun for many patients, and respite for relatives, if only for one afternoon a week. We also formed a support group for bereaved teenagers. At the time I was living in Donegal and so, for geographical reasons, I took responsibility for the Inishowen area.

"In the early days, I was often met at the door by an anxious relative, requesting that I should not tell the patient I was from the hospice. For me this was a reflection of the attitude at that time of a lot of people who did not know or understand what hospice care was about. This attitude changed as the public became more aware of Foyle Hospice and the services provided for the people of Inishowen. Eventually patients and their families were requesting homecare involvement, and it became a normal part of the service offered to many cancer patients by GPs.

"The overall impression of my time in Inishowen is of friendly people who always treated me with great respect and who were generous and hospitable. This was evident in the amount of weight I gained from drinking tea and eating scone bread and other goodies, offered at every house I visited! For me, providing care for patients in their own home was the most rewarding and fulfilling type of nursing. I like to think that care depended on the needs of the patient and their family. Working in homecare was truly holistic care at its best. As well as offering advice on symptom control, supporting the patient emotionally and spiritually at times, I always enjoyed the social chats. I got to know a lot about the lives of patients and their families, and this was important, especially when visiting someone for a long time. Today I have mature plants in my garden, given to me by patients as small cuttings. I have cooking recipes and many small gifts given me by appreciative patients and their families, and I cherish all of these. Most of all, however, I have precious memories of many dignified, courageous people who I will never forget, and from whom I learned so much about life.

"I admit at times it was hard, emotionally more than physically. In the early 1990s, support services were not really available for patients or carers. Foyle

Theresa McSwiney, receiving a cheque of behalf of the McLafferty family, from Patricia McDaid and Fiona Lafferty, from Burt. The proceeds from a 'Night at the Races' were given in memory of their mother Brid McLafferty, (September 1996).

Hospice, under the guidance of Dr Tom, pioneered good palliative care services in Inishowen and it was a privilege for me to be part of this.

"I loved every day of my time working for Foyle Hospice. However, after my own cancer diagnosis, I decide to take some time out. After a break from work, my health improved and I went on to change my career path. I had for many years worked as a counsellor in a voluntary capacity, and I returned to study in order to gain some formal counselling skills and qualifications. I was fortunate enough to be offered a job with the Ulster Cancer Foundation as a counsellor. I am now based at Altnagelvin Hospital and work with patients and family members affected by a cancer diagnosis. My experience at Foyle Hospice has been invaluable to me in my present job.

"Although I no longer work at the hospice, I still feel a great attachment to it. I have so many friends there and will always be grateful to all at the hospice, especially Rosemary Peoples and Dr Tom, for the support given to me professionally and personally."

From the first day of the announcement of a hospice service for Donegal, the people there were very supportive and many joined the weekly draw. Many oth-

Hundreds of Foyle Hospice supporters join Paddy O'Grady during the final stage of the wheelbarrow push to the hospice on Culmore Road. The walk came from Derrybeg (little Derry) to Derry. Tom was reared in the small village of Derrybeg.

Paddy handing over proceeds of the wheelbarrow push to Dr Tom. The wheelbarrow stands in the entrance hall of the hospice and still raises money!

ers began organising events. Dr Don McGinley and Nan McCarron were very active in Moville. In fact Dr Don actually held a raffle with a boat as the prize! This boosted the hospice funds greatly at the time.

In March 1992, following the award of the 'Donegal Person of the Year' to Dr Tom, some members of the Donegal Association in Dublin suggested a wheelbarrow push from Tom's home parish in Gweedore to the Inpatient Unit on the Culmore Road. They raised in excess of £7,000. Indeed the wheelbarrow resides today in the entrance hall of the hospice and still raises money. The main mover behind this novel venture was Paddy O'Grady.

The main impetus in starting the Buncrana Support Group came from Theresa McSwiney and Terri in 1992. Some members began raising funds. They really got going, however, in 1994 when some of the members took part in the first Famine Way Walk. This was organized in memory of the 150th anniversary of the famine in Ireland. This is a 10-mile walk from Doolagh to Louisburgh and has since become a regular sponsored feature in the fundraising calendar of the hospice.

Most of the group belonged to the local church. They bonded well and developed a love for and a dedication to the work of the hospice. Sister Assumpta was a catalyst for this group and is still very active today.

Buncrana Support Group in 1998 presenting a cheque for £6000 (back from left) Noel Doherty, Bridie McDaid, Nicholas Crossan, Sister Assumpta, Kathleen McCartney, Kathleen Coyle, Eugene Coyle. (Front row) Anna McCallion, Teresa McGowan, (hospice nurse) Dr Tom McGinley, Kathleen McKinney, Maisie Grant, Peggy McGlinchey.

Many of the current supporters in the Buncrana Group (2004)

Maisie Grant was one of the founder members. She was an entertainer and a real local character. She used to buy a bottle of whiskey and raffle it round the pubs in Buncrana on a Saturday night, raising money for the hospice. When Maisie moved into a residential home she was no longer able to pursue this weekly round of the pubs! Those of us on that first Famine Walk, including the author and Dr Tom, fondly remember how she entertained us the whole way, in the bus to Westport, and the whole way back. Not only that, she seemed to take over the total entertainment in one of the main pubs in Westport! She died in 2004.

The group has been involved in many fund raising events such as quiz nights, sponsored walks and even an occasional church gate collection which is greatly cherished by local charities. They have had particular success with a 'Mr & Mrs' night and a 'Night at the Races'. This support group remains extremely active after ten years.

When Theresa McSwiney resigned, after her illness, her place in homecare in Inishowen was taken over by Yvonne Martin in June 1997, who continued to be employed by Foyle Hospice. More recently her employment has been taken over by the North Western Health Board in Donegal. Services in Foyle Hospice, both inpatient and daycare, remain available for Donegal patients upon referral by their GP. Some patients may find it more convenient to come to Foyle because it is nearer.

From the very beginning, Tom thought that, one day, the North Western Health Board in Donegal and the Western Health and Social Services in Derry would join up to provide a regional oncology service. While this hope may be realised in the future, the existing coordinated services, which transcend the border, have meant that patients, throughout the entire North-West, have been able to receive the best of modern palliative care, irrespective of class, creed or political label. This has come about as the result of the urgent needs of one small boy and the vision of one doctor, Dr Tom.

Dr Tom is honoured by the Donegal Association in Dublin for his initiative and vision in providing palliative care services for the people of Donegal. Left of Tom, Kathleen Sheerin, President of the Donegal Association.

Chapter Nine

The Spiritual Heart of the Hospice

"Yea though I walk through the valley of the shadow of death, I will fear no evil for thou art with me, thy rod and thy staff they comfort me" Psalm 23

The philosophy of Foyle Hospice is based firmly on a Christian ethic. Most patients come from a background in the Christian faith, whatever denomination they may belong to. In keeping with the philosophy of 'building bridges' the hospice has insisted, from the beginning, that it would be inter-denominational and, when the need presented itself, inter-faith.

To this end the four main denominations within the Foyle area were invited to appoint chaplains. By far the largest congregation is Roman Catholic followed by Church of Ireland, Presbyterian and Methodist. The four chaplains, together, were instrumental in organising two events a year, one being a service to celebrate the switching on of the Christmas Lights and the other a commemorative Thanksgiving Service held during June. Inter-denominational services are well attended and the atmosphere deeply spiritual and often emotional.

The need for spiritual sustenance and advice at such a time in the journey of life is vital. The four chaplains attend as and when required. At such a difficult time in their life, the patient, faced with the prospect of dying, needs the spiritual comfort from their clergy. Care and love of family and friends becomes foremost. Fear often manifests, especially fear of the unknown. All of these spiritual subjects are addressed by the chaplains who listen with patient and kindly hearts.

The Chapel

An essential area reserved for worship was designed into the original plans for the hospice. The chapel has become one of the most restful and peaceful areas of the building. The furniture was originally purchased from funds raised by the Eglinton Hospice Support Group.

Table and chairs, lectern and cross blend well with white walls and the beautiful wooden ceiling.

A beautiful stained glass window illuminated at night and visible from inside and outside.

Bishop Edward Daly – Chaplain

One of the most cheery and friendly faces seen around the hospice, virtually on a daily basis, is that of Bishop Edward.

He was Bishop of Derry from 1974 through to his retirement, on health grounds, in 1993. He then became chaplain for the hospice and is ably assisted by Father Eamon Graham when the need arises. Bishop Daly serves as President of the hospice and is greatly loved by staff and patients of all faiths.

Bishop Daly says, "For the last ten years, my ministry has been dedicated to accompanying people and their families on that journey, their last few weeks and months of their pilgrimage through life." This is how he speaks in the foreword of a wonderful little book launched in late 2004 by *Veritas Publications* of Dublin, (*'Do Not Let Your Hearts Be Troubled'*). I recommend this book be read by people of all Christian denominations and those of other faiths and, indeed, of none.

Bishop Edward Daly

It records great insight into the world of being a chaplain in a hospice. "I have found," Bishop Daly says, "that my experience of serious illness and cancer was some assistance to me in ministering to those undergoing similar experience, albeit more acute." He himself had a malignant tumour removed from the kidney in 1977. He then suffered a moderate stroke in 1993. In 1999, he had a further tumour removed from his lung which proved to be a secondary from the kidney. He is still going strong!

'Peace I bequeath to you, my own peace I give you, a peace the world cannot give, this is my gift to you. Do not let your hearts be troubled or afraid.' (John 14:27)

In his chapter on the hospice itself, he goes on to say: "The nearby Foyle Bridge was adopted as the symbol or logo of the hospice – because the hospice is truly a bridge between both sides of the city, between both communities in the North-West and is also, for many, the bridge between this life and the next."

He very touchingly refers to the situation when patients are admitted to the hospice. Often changed by the disease itself and/or by treatments he says, "Their self-esteem has suffered. Many of them are frightened and bewildered. Their life and the lives of their families have been turned upside down. Future plans have been put on hold. The words of Jesus in St Matthew's Gospel often come to mind, *'Come to me, all you who labour and are overburdened, and I will give you rest. Shoulder my yoke and learn from me, for I am gentle and humble in heart, and you will find rest for your souls.'* (Matthew 11:28-30) That quotation is particularly apt for a hospice or hospice care. People who experience a long battle with cancer are certainly overburdened."

Many other spiritual insights are scattered throughout this little gem of a book. Right at the end, on the very last page, he relates a moving and poignant episode. "I remember sitting with a patient on a lovely autumn evening a few years ago. It was just getting dark. We had prayed together and we are both sitting and looking out the window at the lights of the traffic busily moving to and fro on the Foyle Bridge. She had told me earlier about how peaceful and happy she was. Then she smiled and quietly said to me, 'This is like God's waiting room.'"

Father Eamon Graham – Assistant Chaplain

Father Eamon is an open, friendly and tolerant man. He explained that he had taken over from Father Crilly some years previous and, while Bishop Daly is the official Chaplain, he would deputise when requested.

He meets with the other three chaplains twice a year to plan the inter-denominational services.

"You never leave the hospice without having laughed or smiled," he said. "If it happened I was visited with a terminal illness I would love to spend my last days in the hospice." Father Eamon has a very special place in his heart for the hospice where, he says, "Sickness and death are treated as part of life and not

Father Eamon Graham

separate from it." He longed to see the hospice philosophy spread right out into society, as he wistfully commented, "All the petty differences within our society melt away in the hospice."

Rev. Matthew Moore – Church of Ireland Chaplain

Rev. Matt Moore, a man of gentle humour, has been the incumbent in St Peter's as well as Muff & Culmore, since 1996. Canon Leslie McConachie was the previous chaplain, now retired. Rev. Moore says, "Many Church of Ireland patients who come to the hospice would prefer their rector from their own parish." He added, "The hospice would ring me 'on demand' so to speak; or indeed the parish might inform me when a patient is being admitted."

He is delighted to work with the other three chaplains when they organise the inter-denominational services. They all agree the programme for these services.

Rev. Matthew Moore

"Attending patients needs delicacy," says Rev. Moore, "It is not only a preparation of the patient for death, but the family needs support as well. There is a spiritual preparation and learning to cope."

He is so impressed by the "great compassion and dedication of the staff". He goes on to say, "The hospice is so different. It's not like a hospital. There is such peace and quiet." Trying to summarise the atmosphere in a single sentence he stated: "The presence of God is in this hospice."

Rev. Joe McCormick – Presbyterian Chaplain

Rev. Joe is a caring man who makes those he meets feel at ease. He has now been chaplain for about five years and feels "very much part of the hospice family from the top down". He is very supportive of the inter-denominational services and states that, "All my relations with colleagues of other denominations have been very amiable."

Rev. Joe McCormick

When working in Letterkenny he attended a course on palliative care and likes to keep up with current issues in this field. "Presbyterians," he says, "like to have their own minister attend them but I am available any time the hospice needs me. Families from my own congregation have been very pleased. Any who have had loved ones die in the hospice would often return to meet with staff again. They have a great appreciation of what was done for them, and they experience the peace and tranquillity of the place."

The Rev. McCormick added. "Just being there for them was good. One doesn't have to speak." Then he said, "I count it a privilege to share the compassion of the love of God at this time of intimacy."

Rev. Sam McGuffin – Methodist Minister

Rev. Sam has been more than two years in his post as chaplain. He is a jolly but intense man, keenly focused on bettering relations between the denominations. He said, "Each minister stays eight years on a circuit (equivalent to a parish) before moving on." He covers Derry, Strabane, Culdaff to Limavady, seven churches in all and about 1500 parishioners.

Rev. Sam McGuffin

He was associated with the Northern Ireland Hospice when he worked in Belfast and occasionally took the 'act of worship'. It was there he became familiar with hospice philosophy and was very impressed with the care and attention given to patients. "The hospice gives me a ring when a member of my congregation is admitted."

He looks forward to participating in the inter-denominational services held at the hospice.

'Lord, make me a channel of Thy peace, where there is hatred may I bring love; where there is injury, pardon; where there is doubt, faith; where there is despair, hope; where there is darkness, light; and where there is sadness, joy. O Divine Lover, grant that we may not so much seek to be consoled as to console; to be understood as to understand; to be loved as to love; for it is in giving that we receive, it is in pardoning that we are pardoned, and it is in dying that we are born to eternal life.

St Francis of Assisi.

Chapter Ten

'Two Little Girls' Remember

Together, Clare and Emma had the honour of opening the hospice in June 1991 when they were eight years old. Both had lost mothers to cancer some years previously. They and their fathers had many and difficult struggles over the subsequent years.

Dr McGinley with the girls and their fathers some time before the official opening. (Left) Pat and Clare McLaughlin, (right) Norman and Emma Robinson. (1991)

Clare McLaughlin

"I was so young when mummy [Bernadette] died," said Clare. "I was about three or four. I used to stay with an uncle and an aunt while Daddy went to Belvoir Park Hospital to be with mum. She lost all her hair with the chemo." Clare was fortunate that her father was a teacher and was able to take her into school while she was only three. Clare went on to say that, although she cannot recollect much of her mother's death, she remembers "feeling the grief of my Dad

Currently Clare is studying art in Belfast

as well as my brothers' and sisters'". She remembers the support given by the homecare team. "We had so much help from so many – of course Hannah and Rosemary, hospice nurses, were central. Dad was a 'rock'.

"He came home from school did washing, cooking, cleaning and took us horse-riding and he never complained."

Clare says that it is only now she can fully appreciate what her father did for her. "I was excited when I was asked, with Emma, to open the hospice, and Daddy was very pleased. Emma and I were the youngest in our families and about the same age. I remember going to Pat Cowley's house [artist] where he took photographs of both of us for an oil painting."

Oil painting by Pat Cowley commissioned by the Orange Order. This shows Clare and Emma looking across the river at the hospice site.

Clare mused, "I have two older brothers and a sister. It took a long time for the family to open up and talk about Mum. Only now, in the last few years, we've been able to talk. There was a lot of pain for many years."

Clare is now studying art in Belfast. "Losing Mummy has made me a stronger more independent person. I've had to do many things, especially in the house, that other children my age perhaps didn't do."

Clare's father Pat

At the time of Berna's death Pat was glad that he had been a teacher. He was able to take Clare into his school when she was only three. Dr McGinley was Berna's doctor and she showed a great interest in the work of the hospice. "She became quite excited at the prospect of a hospice being built," said Pat. "In fact it was Hollybush Primary School that was the first school to raise funds for the hospice (1983).

"It was around that time that Berna was diagnosed with breast cancer. When she heard the diagnosis she said to me, 'I am too young and have no time to be sick.' From then on Hannah and Rosemary, recently trained in hospice home-care, began to play a big part in her life. They were invaluable and always reinforced the positive. She had quite a difficult time with the chemotherapy. Finally Berna died on 14th February, 1987 at home with the children. Rosemary and Hannah talked to the children about feelings in an easy and gentle way."

Pat McLaughlin, principal of Hollybush Primary School, presenting a cheque to Dr Tom McGinley. In the centre are joint organisers of the project, Mrs Geraldine Curran and Mrs Colette Craig.

Emma Anderson (neé Robinson)

Emma was just nine years of age when she was invited to assist in opening the hospice. Her mother had died from cancer in 1985 when she was only three. "I had two older sisters." she said, "When I went to primary school, I began to realise I didn't have a Mum." Emma went on to say, "Auntie Natalie, who was Mum's sister, became very supportive and I spent a lot of time with her." Emma continued, "While it made me more independent I find that, even after all these years, I still grieve." She now realises just what an honour it had been to be asked to open the hospice.

In April 2004, she married Lee. She thinks the hospice is an "absolutely brilliant place" and helps patients and their families. "I went down before I got married," she said, "and donated a sum of money rather than give 'wedding favours' to the guests."

Emma and Lee. Happily married in 2004

Emma's father Norman

"Paula, my wife, was diagnosed with stomach cancer in 1984. She went on to have an operation but it had already spread to other organs. She chose to have chemotherapy but had quite severe side effects." At the time Paula was becoming very ill, Emma was not yet four and her other two sisters, Stacey and Jenny, were two and nine respectively. After she was discharged from hospital, Hannah and Rosemary began attending Paula. She also had a visit from Berna McLaughlin who had recently been diagnosed with cancer. She told Paula, "I'm learning to live with it, not dying of it." Norman, who was a self-employed joiner, gave up his work to devote himself full-time to caring for Paula. She subsequently died peacefully on 29th December, 1985 at home. He took the girls to the grave to try and explain what had happened and told them that "mummy had gone to heaven".

Norman felt the very positive influence of both hospice nurses. He felt that they were not just interested in Paula but took a special interest in the girls as well as himself.

"Dr Tom came to see me in 1991 and asked would I consider if one of the girls would officially open the hospice. I was delighted and we chose Emma. In fact, all three of my girls were excited and were all present on that historic day."

Both Clare and Emma took part in a subsequent TV documentary about the hospice entitled 'Life is a Journey'.

'Life is a Journey'
"My Most Fulfilling Television Experience"
Chris Orr, producer and director, recollects
his time at the Hospice in January 1999.

I went to make a short news piece on Foyle Hospice for the new local Channel 9 TV station. After spending a day at the hospice, I was so impressed by what I saw that I decided to make a one hour programme in Jan 1999. At first, I was very nervous of even going into the hospice as a dear friend of mine had died there a short time previously. By the end of the first day of filming with the crew, however, I felt that it was quite simply one of the most incredible places I had ever set foot in. I was amazed at not only the sense of peace, but also the humour amongst staff and patients. There was no fear in the building, and by the time I had finished making the programme two months later, I felt that I did not want to leave, knowing that God's presence permeated the whole building. I interviewed people who had little time to live, relations of those who had already died, as well as two people who recovered and are still alive and well today. Everyone was more than willing to cooperate in the programme making. I remember one patient, who I thought was too close to the end to be interviewed. He came and asked me why I was not including him in the programme? Hence, the programme was dedicated to Eugene McGilloway for his courage in telling his story. One weekend, while we were filming, five patients died and I was totally amazed at how Dr Tom McGinley could be so upset over each patient. Medical staff generally can get hardened to seeing people die but Tom looks on each patient as a friend, which sets him apart as one of life's truly amazing people. There is no doubt in my mind that he is a man who has been blessed by God with a mission to help and care for people when they need it the most. When he finally retires, he should be remembered for his unselfish love for human beings, which is above and beyond the call of duty.

It was also a privilege to interview Clare and Emma, who officially opened the hospice, and to meet their families. It was very brave of them to go on-camera, but then they are very special too.

I was impressed also with Bishop Edward Daly who believes that his retirement work at the Foyle Hospice is the most fulfilling yet in his life, and he was so welcomed by people of all denominations.

In my 25 years in television, I regard 'Life is a Journey' as my most fulfilling programme to make. People are amazed when I say that it was the easiest. This was because the people who I interviewed, and the staff, who are angels anyway, made it all so easy.

Chris's programme was repeated on Channel 9 from time to time over the years. There was positive feedback for the hospice, from viewers, each time it was shown.

Chapter Eleven

The Hospice Day Centre

In this world we are influenced by two sentiments, Joy and Pain. Joy gives us wings! In times of joy our strength is more vital, our intellect keener, and our understanding less clouded. We seem better able to cope with the world and to find our sphere of usefulness. There is no human being untouched by these two influences; but all the sorrow and the grief that exist come from the world of matter — the spiritual world bestows only the joy.

Bahá'í Writings

The Foyle Hospice services developed well through the 1990s. High standards of nursing, and the caring and nurturing atmosphere were to become the greatest publicity for the palliative care offered. In January 1999, Dr Tom explained to Trustees that services needed to be developed further with specific emphasis on a daycare centre. This separate building in the grounds of the hospice would facilitate patients receiving palliative care at home to attend one or two days a week. They could avail themselves of the various therapies and take part in various pastimes such as music and art therapy. Hairdos would be a popular option for females. And they would benefit from meeting others on a similar journey.

This major development would cost approximately £750,000 to build and in excess of £100,000 for annual running costs. Dr McGinley was also very keen to move the fundraising centre from Crawford Square to the hospice site on Culmore Road. This major responsibility for raising funds was to be taken over by a voluntary fundraising group. They were requested to be innovative in finding new ideas for fundraising. The project went out to tender and Conway and Sons were appointed as builders along with the original architects, Smyth and McMurtry from Limavady. Work commenced in January 2000.

Subsequently Julia McIvor was appointed Nurse Manager for the unit, along with two staff nurses, Teresa McGowan and Ruth Ferris.

The opening date was set for 1st May, 2002 with two of the early homecare sisters, Teresa McSwiney and Gretta Linehan, doing the honours of officially opening the unit. Mayor Mildred Garfield was invited to attend. The weather was glorious, just as it had been for the opening of the Inpatient Unit on 20th June, 1991.

Architect's painting of the new Day Centre. (Left) Jim McMurtry (architect), Jack McCauley (Quantity Surveyor), Ciarán McGinley (Project Manager), Declan Conway (Building Contractor), Jim Guy (Trustee) and Tom McGinley.

Dr Tom cutting the first sod for the new Day Centre. (From left) Trustees Michael McCafferty and Jim Guy, Ciarán McGinley, (Coordinator of the Day Centre Project), Hannah Healy, Dr Tom, Bishop Edward Daly and Rosemary Peoples.

The Hospice Day Centre and Fundraising Centre on schedule!

On April 11th, 2002, a few weeks prior to the official opening, the Day Centre was honoured with a visit from the President of the Republic of Ireland, Mary McAleese, and her husband Martin. They were delighted with the building and wished the hospice well for the future.

Dr Tom escorting President Mary McAleese towards the new Day Centre.

*Pausing during her visit to the Day Hospice is President Mary McAleese together with
Julia McIvor (left) and (right) Kathleen Boyle (volunteer) and Teresa McGowan.*

*Nurses Gretta Linehan and Teresa McSwiney opening the new Day Centre flanked
by Dr Tom and Mayor Mildred Garfield. (1st May, 2000)*

Julia McIvor, Nurse Manager of the Day Centre

Staff Nurse Teresa McGowan / Staff Nurse Ruth Ferris

The welcoming entrance hall of the Day Centre

Part of the Day Centre overlooking Foyle Bridge.
Grazing horses add to the relaxing atmosphere.

144

The Day Centre nestling in the beautiful hospice grounds.

Hugh Kelly surrounded by staff, volunteers and other patients attending the Daycare Centre. Hugh died at home on 30th September, 2003. On his right is Deirdre Harkin who died at home on 7th September, 2005. (Back left) Helen Dunwoody, cook, whose scones are "out of this world", says Dr Tom.

Enjoying a joke and a wee cuppa!

Sheila, volunteer hairdresser, putting the finishing touches to Margaret Boyle's hair.

Maureen Harvey attended by Diane, beauty therapist.

The arts feature strongly in the Day Centre. (From left) Michelle Wooderson, (music therapist), Máire Mullan,(artist), Jim McConnell, (artist) and Dr Tom. These artists have raised significant funds from exhibitions of their work.

A sunny day in spring. Staff and patients from the Day Centre and the Inpatient Unit enjoy the blossoms.

George Hamilton, patient at the Day Centre, together with Donna and Edel.

Charlie McCallion's pride and joy. Luxury transport for patients. Since 1991, Charlie has been helping in the gardens. "I always look forward to coming here. It's so peaceful. But it's hard to keep up with 'the Doctor' when he decides to get stuck into the gardens!" Charlie had been a bus-driver by profession. He retired in 2003 and was a natural choice for driver of the hospice minibus.

Margaret Taylor – Day Centre Cook. Margaret helped to set up the kitchen in the main hospice in 1991 and covered staff holidays and sickness. She later left for some seven years, returning as cook in the Daycare Centre when Helen Dunwoody retired from that post in July 2004. Margaret was a former tutor in cooking at the North West Institute.

Joan Cheetam, volunteer at the Day Centre.

Finvola ('Vola') Doherty

Vola comes from Dungiven. She has attended the Day Hospice for two years. Four years previously, she was diagnosed as having motor neurone disease. "For a long time before that," says Vola, "I was trying to find my way around things. I realised I was getting weaker but decided to keep it from the family. I thought I had Parkinson's Disease." The neurologist had excluded MS but felt that MND was a possibility. Apparently it had presented in a very unusual way, and it was eventually confirmed.

Vola loves coming to the Day Hospice. "It lifts you, and all the patients are on the same journey. They all have something special to offer. No one talks about dying. Coming here is great, you can off-load, and all the nursing staff are out this world."

Freddie Doherty was a patient in the Day Centre. He was encouraged to take up art and became so accomplished that he was invited to hold his own exhibition at the Gasworks Centre in the Bogside. This summer photograph was taken in 2004. Freddie died in July 2005 in the Inpatient Unit. Also in the picture are Dr Tom and Teresa McGowan. Charlie seems to have a flea in his ear!

Chapter Twelve

Fundraising

Money is the lifeblood of any project but especially a voluntary project. It relies largely on the kindness, generosity and sacrifice of the public. While Foyle Hospice is subsidised by statutory bodies, about 70% of all funding must be raised by the hard work of fundraising and from voluntary donation. In 1983, the small steering committee of three had no idea that well over a million pounds would be needed for the building of the Inpatient Unit. Faith in the huge generosity of the people of the North-West kept them going. During those years, and up to the present time, hospice support groups have played a very big part in raising large sums.

When the Weekly Draw was launched on 12th December 1985, membership rose to about three thousand, each member paying £1 a week. The draw was to become the backbone of fundraising. The promoters were the muscles and sinews. These people have been dedicated and tireless workers.

Alistair Kinkaid – Fundraiser

In 1987, Alistair was appointed to coordinate the increasing number of fundraising events. Such was his personality that he gelled well with people. His main responsibility was the Weekly Draw. He also encouraged the various support groups in their early work.

Unfortunately, in early January of 1998, he was diagnosed with cancer of the lung. During the last few weeks of his life, he was fully aware of the rapid deterioration of his condition and totally accepted his impending death. He died peacefully in the hospice on 1st April. Dr McGinley, in praising his work, said in '*The Sentinel*' of April 8th of that year:

"He displayed great courage and total belief in his Christian faith, and in the hospice philosophy that death is a natural process not to be feared or denied. His preparation was meticulous. He had the great ability of reaching out to all sections of the community and everyone instantly warmed to his cheery and friendly personality. His deep affection for close family and the wider circle will always remain outstanding in our memory. He especially loved the very young and the very old. However he held a special place in his heart for the disabled of our society. He will be sadly missed."

Alistair was survived by his wife Dorothy and his children Stephen and Joanne.

Joan Brown

Joan has been with the hospice since the early days. She has warm memories of working in Crawford Square. "I joined the Foyle Hospice Fundraising Team in 1988 as an ACE worker, where I worked closely with the Fundraising Coordinator Alistair Kinkaid. It was a time of great excitement to be part of the team and a great honour for me. After Alistair's premature death, I took responsibility for the Weekly Draw. I also started up a thrift shop for clothes and bric-a-brac. This was the first successful shop and ran for some time, raising significant amounts for the campaign at that time. Then the Copper Hunt collections were gaining momentum and it kept us all busy counting the many thousands of coins. I have made a lot of friends during my journey from the early days of the hospice. It has been a wonderful experience. Just to be there to see Dr McGinley's dream come true was a very emotional time for everyone. Today I work as part of a much larger team at the new Fundraising Centre based in the grounds of the Inpatient Unit."

Ciarán McGinley – Fundraising Manager and Public Relations Officer

Ciarán has been working for the hospice in various capacities on a voluntary basis since he was in his teens. He would have been very aware of his father's earliest plans for establishing a hospice. His first direct involvement was helping with the early female mini-marathons as well as on flag days. "I vividly remember," he says, "going with Dad on a pub crawl carrying buckets to collect money on the night of the flag days. People were quite amazed to see two men wearing pioneer pins going in and out of pubs!

Ciarán McGinley.

(From left) Teresa and Rita, workers in the Crawford Sq. shop, together with customers.

The Fundraising Centre.

153

"When I was a student at college in Birmingham, Dad used to stay with me on a regular basis. He took the opportunity to visit various hospices in the surrounding area, especially the local ones, St Mary's Hospice and the Compton Hospice in Wolverhampton. He would also visit the Dorothy House Hospice in Bath and St Luke's Hospice in Sheffield. He gave two lectures a year to the other students in my college, one on sports injuries and the other on terminal care. When I finished my course, and started working locally, I regularly accompanied him as he travelled the length and breadth of Ireland giving lectures about hospice-type care.

"He worked very closely with the Irish Cancer Society in Dublin, whose main aim was to set up homecare services in various areas. I remember well trips to Killarney, Drogheda, Galway, Navan and the Midlands. I did the driving!

"Gradually I absorbed the concepts and philosophy of hospice care. I slowly began to realise the extent of what he was doing and I became heavily involved in fundraising. In 1990 Dad and I, along with Bernie Mount and Pat McArt, took part in the London Marathon and raised approximately £25,000. This money was to furnish the spacious front hall of the hospice.

Runners getting ready for a jog in preparation for the London Marathon (1990). (From left) Pat McArt, Ciarán McGinley, Bernie Mount and Tom McGinley. Seán Coyle (Radio Foyle) is there for encouragement!

"In 1994, Dad had suggested I help to set up a voluntary fundraising group with emphasis on new initiatives for raising money. He felt that events should not in any way interfere with existing fundraising strategies. He was of the opinion that this money would be required to add on a purpose-built Daycare Unit as well as providing a fundraising unit on the same site. The main events undertaken by the fundraising group were the New York and Boston marathons, trips to Peru, Nepal, China and the Grand Canyon. The Peru trip raised £80,000. The other members of this group included Terri Sythes, Neil Doherty, Noel McMonagle, Joe Morrison and Eddie O'Hagan among others."

A very large sum raised from running the New York Marathon in 1994. (From left) Ciarán McGinley, Dr Tom, Bridgeen Moore, Evelyn Doherty and Joe Morrison.

Members of the Foyle Hospice North-West Marathon Group presenting a cheque for £34,000 raised from the Boston Marathon, 1996.

£7,000 raised by the Voluntary Fundraising Group during late 1996. (Back row, l-r) Robbie Butler, Paul McGilloway, Ed Quigley, Colin Roberts, Gary McGee and Colm Wilkinson. (Middle row, l-r) Jason Ferguson, Paul McLaughlin, Mura Henry, Evelyn Doherty, Carmel McGee, Liam Bonner. (Front row, l-r) Michael Farren, Noel McMonagle, Dr Tom, Ciarán McGinley and Francie Brannon. Colm Wilkinson died in January 2000 at Altnagelvin Hospital from Non-Hodgkin's Lymphoma. His wife Bernadette works in the hospice office.

In September 2000, Ciarán arranged for an 18-month secondment from his health service job in chiropody to take up post as Project Manager for the new Daycare Centre. Subsequently the Trustees decided that a fulltime fundraising manager was essential and the job was advertised. Ciarán continues, "I applied immediately and happily my interview was successful. It was a dream come true. Passion for the hospice drives me and I'm proud of what my father has established for the people of the North-West. Fundraising has changed in the last four to five years. Many other charities are out there competing for the same money. Though the hospice sells itself in many ways, it needed an injection of new ideas in order to 'keep ahead of the game'."

Most of Ciarán's team was already in place when he took over. Now, however, he manages them in a different way. Currently there are more budget controls and more spending on advertising for instance. They regularly sit down as a team and make great efforts to meet targets. Fundraising will always be an essential need for the smooth running of all the various services that are offered by the hospice teams.

Talking to members of the team, it is clear to see that Ciarán has a very dedicated and loyal band of workers. Each member has their duties. Alex does collections and Joan oversees the Weekly Draw. This draw was started by the Prehen Support Group and was the back-bone of fundraising especially in the early years. Currently it has about 6,000 members paying a pound a week.

Members of the team hard at work – Rachel, Anita and Ciarán.

Some of the core team in the Fundraising Centre. (Standing) Rachael Osbourne, Marcella Keogh, Ciarán McGinley. (Sitting) Anita Bradley and Teresa Brennick. Not included are Ailbhe McDaid and Louise McElhinney, who is part-time. Both are a great bonus to the team.

The Copper Hunt started out with the spare pennies people threw into a cardboard box in shops. Dr Tom was worried that people would think they could only put coppers in the box. He arranged for a change of name to Coin Hunt. Today it raises the staggering sum of over £200,000 yearly! The logistics of counting the tons of donated coins are quite something, never mind the lifting work involved. Alex McLaughlin does many of these bank runs.

Marcella with the tons of coin.

Alex McLaughlin, driver, collector and 'general dogsbody' according to him!

The Foyle Hospice Newsletter was started in November 2000.

158

Ciarán feels there is a sense of ownership by the community. "They can see what their money is doing and has done. In fact, we started a Newsletter in November 2000, which goes out twice a year. There's a circulation of around 6400. Everyone in the draw, and donors as well, gets a copy. There's brilliant feedback. It keeps people informed of the work of the Hospice and publicly thanks them for their ongoing support."

Noel McMonagle was appointed Community Fundraiser and took up his post on 3rd January, 2005. He had been involved with the Voluntary

Noel McMonagle,
Community Fundraiser.

Fundraising Group for many years and was the organiser for events such as the London Marathon and the Great North Run. His first big venture, after his appointment, was the 'Night at the Races' at the Lifford dog track. Local business man, Cathal Curley, was the chairman and main initiator of this huge event, which raised a staggering £120,000 for hospice funds.

Hospice Shops – More than Selling

Once the property in Crawford Square was purchased in 1984, it became a hive of energy for fundraising as well as an office for the Homecare Service. Some time after this Joan Brown, who started as an ACE worker, organised a thrift shop for clothes and bric-a-brac. This was the first successful hospice shop and ran for some time, raising significant amounts for the campaign at that time.

Other temporary shops had existed, before the one in Crawford Square, the earliest being set up during early 1984. Dr Keith negotiated the use of a temporary building at Lane's Mall in Clarendon Street. This also acted as the first information centre for the hospice.

The Castlederg Hospice Shop

Teresa Young saw her father-in-law die painfully from bone cancer. This was in the early 1990s. Teresa said, "We were not too familiar about the work of the hospice at that time." She went on, "I was desperate and a local priest suggested the hospice. My father-in-law was in so much pain that I rang the hospice and spoke to Terri. I was advised to see the GP for an urgent referral. He was admitted the same day but, sadly, died some twelve hours later. I found the hospice homely, peaceful and it had a wonderful family feeling."

It is customary for members of staff to have a service before the remains leave the hospice. The staff then walk behind the coffin for some distance along the driveway. Teresa continued, "One of the staff, Teresa McGowan, was walking behind the coffin and I said to her that we'd run a dance after it was all over."

She kept her promise and indeed organised many dances, as well as teas and other events. She raised almost £10,000 and then sold some 115 tickets for the £100 Ticket Millennium Draw in 2000.

Then Teresa thought, "Why do I keep going to people pestering them for money and for tickets? Why don't I get them to come to me? I began researching charity shops for about six months. I must have visited 40-50 from here to Dublin. Some I found were absolute rubbish while others were impressive. In general I felt the prices were too high and the quality variable. Anyhow, I got an empty shop at the bottom of the town. Then I found a store at the top of the town. At the time it looked like a building site. I rented this from Michael Gribben. He had reconstructed the old building and was kind enough to rent it at a very reasonable cost. We opened on the 27th September, 2003. From then till July '04, we must have raised about £18,000."

The hospice purchased a van which was essential for collections and deliveries. This van was bought from money raised from car-boot sales run by Bernadette McGoldrick. She systematically went to one or two a week making anything from £100-£150 per time. Even the diesel for the van was donated.

Teresa and Vincent Young presenting a cheque for £1,050 to Dr Tom and Teresa. This money was the proceeds from a Barn Dance held in Maguire's Bar, Newtownstewart in August 1997.

The hospice shop at the lower end of Castlederg.

Teresa Young, founder of the shop, second from the right. Other members of her team are Andrew Birney, Margaret Crees and Jean McBride.

"The shop is run by volunteers," says Teresa. "Sub-standard clothing is recycled which helps pay the rent for the large store in the upper part of the town. Items from cups and jewellery to furniture and clothes keep pouring in. Customers come from all over, including Donegal."

It is significant that they opened on 27th September, 2003. This was Teresa's sister, Maureen Campbell's birthday. She is one of her most faithful helpers. Teresa had gone with some ladies to see around the hospice. "While there," she said, "I picked up some advice from Dr Tom which was to be a great help to Maureen. She was quickly diagnosed with cancer of the breast and speedily operated on. She then had chemotherapy followed by radiotherapy. She came through and is now one of the most stalwart of volunteers. Thanks to Dr McGinley's wise advice and my prompt action, my sister is alive today."

As well as Maureen, Teresa has many helpers. Among them are Margaret Crees and Jean McBride. Michael Gribben, owner of the store as well as van-driver, is a most valuable member of the team.

Michael Gribben

The shop at the lower end of the town opens from 10.30am - 4.30pm, five days a week. Teresa says, "The hospice, and the shop itself, have been a uniting force in a very divided town. Sadly, cancer hits old and young, black and white, Catholic and Protestant. We all work to raise the much needed funds for running the hospice."

The Hospice Shop – Shipquay Street, Derry

After her mother's death in January 2004, Mary Gallagher decided she wanted to 'do something'. She already helped charities by visiting Romania three or four times a year. She realised that Derry currently had no hospice thrift shop. She spoke with Ciarán who is the Fundraising Manager. "It all happened in about one day, last September", says Mary. "I was sitting in Shipquay Street and saw rooms for rent. I immediately rang the owner who was extremely helpful. He offered it at once for a reasonable rent and it was all tied up that day. "McElhinney's of Ballybofey, the well-known department stores, were extremely helpful. John McElhinney, himself, gave us fittings. Stock poured in and we opened at the end of November 2004."

Three of Mary's team. (From left) Teresa Doherty, Carmel Egan, Mary, and Kay Gallagher.

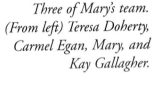

Looking into the new hospice shop in Shipquay Street. It is situated just above Ken McGilloway's Art Gallery. Ken is one of the Trustees of Foyle Hospice.

Mary is assisted by a great team of some 17 people who cover 12 shifts weekly. They open six days a week. Mary is extremely enthusiastic about the success of the shop. She says, "There has been such a great response so far, and it is really good to have a focus for the hospice in the heart of the city. They leave money for the hospice and all sorts of things. In other words they don't just come to buy or leave in items. I am so glad there is this little haven where people can even just come in for a chat."

Musicals

In the 1980s, the name of T.C. Doherty was on many a lip. His talent as a composer led to him creating five musicals including Ebenezer and Starchild (his fifth). All proceeds of these musicals were presented to Foyle Hospice and assisted greatly in the boosting of much needed funds at that time prior to the opening of the Inpatient Unit.

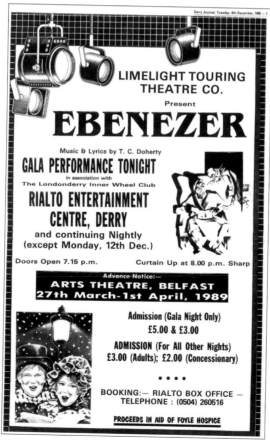

T.C. Doherty, presents a cheque for £5,000 in May 1988, the proceeds of Starlight, to Dr Tom McGinley. (From left), Hugh Farren, who played the title role, Ciarán McGinley, P.R.O, and Peggy Doherty, a member of the production team.

Walking, Running and Climbing etc.
Fundraising efforts exerted for the
hospice all over the world

From the time of the first Foyle Hospice Female Run, the scene was set for runs, marathons, climbing expeditions and cycle rides. Indeed there has been an endless combination of events involving walking, running and climbing to raise funds for the building and running of the hospice. Marathons have been run in many cities for the hospice. Expeditions have set off to Peru, Nepal, China, the Grand Canyon, the Four Peaks in the UK, Croagh Patrick in Mayo and so on. The list is endless. There have also been the more exotic adventures such as abseiling and parachute jumping.

There is something symbolic about so many exercising to keep fit and healthy in order to help those who need palliative care. The love and generosity expressed by so many volunteers is the heart and lifeblood of the hospice and will always be so. In this chapter we can only mention a few of the events and people involved.

The finish of the first Foyle Hospice Female Run in 1984

Malin Head   Mizen Head

Tired but enthusiastic bike riders passing the front of the hospice on the
Culmore Road. They had come from Mizen Head, at the other end of
Ireland, and were heading for Malin.

Climbing High for the Hospice
Nepal: January 2000

This trek to Nepal raised £45,000 for the hospice. Sadly, Colm Wilkinson, who planned to travel on the trip, had died. Here the group is preparing to honour Colm, with the Hindu custom of floating prayers down the river in a basket. This is done in memory of a loved one.

The group visits children suffering from leprosy. They assisted the centre with their own personal money.

China: October 2001

Combined group of trekkers from Foyle and the Southern Area (Newry) hospices sitting on the Great Wall of China! They raised £60,000 for hospice funds.

Grand Canyon: September 2002

Some of a party of 40 Foyle Hospice trekkers at the Grand Canyon. (From left) Robbie Butler, John Leonard, Paddy McFadden and Gavin McShane. £70,000 was raised for the hospice.

Peru: October 2003

Intrepid climbers approaching the lost city of the Incas, Machu Pichu. This trip raised £82,000 for hospice funds.

The Four Peaks: 2004
Scaffel Pike, Ben Nevis, Slieve Donard & Snowdon inside 48 hours!

Stalwart climbers ready to tackle the Four Peaks, 2004. They came from Foyle and St Rocco's (Warrington) hospices. (Ciarán, second from left).

Martin Byrne on top of the world

The peak of fitness. Our very own Bridgeen, Paddy and Jim and two fundraisers from St Rocco's Hospice in Warrington

The First Famine Way Walk

Every year a group go on the famous Famine Way Walk near Louisbourg and Croagh Patrick in Mayo. This event has become traditional. Those who are more energetic climb Croagh Patrick. All raise funds for the hospice.

The author, Dr Keith, and Dr Tom with walkers arriving in Louisbourg in 1994 for the first Famine Way Walk. Teresa McGowan is well wrapped in her Aran sweater (middle front row).

Staff of Aberfoyle Surgery presenting £1,500, to Dr Tom, proceeds of the Famine Way Walk, 1995. (From left) Jean Begley, Eileen O'Neill, Susanne Gillespie, Marie Boyle, Joanne Murphy and Marcelline Doherty. Absent from the picture are Annette McCarron, Marie Hutton and Deirdre Coady. The cheque brought the total raised by various local groups on the walk to £15,000.

The author, who is still amongst the less energetic, determined to do the walk that year. Later he recorded a few memories of his 'struggle'!

"Wee Buns, Dr Munro!"

For some the ten mile Famine Walk is a 'wee dawdle'. For me it was a major challenge. I hadn't attempted ten miles non-stop since I was 19, when I walked the Mourne Wall Walk – some 23 miles over the mountains. Now at 51, I had managed the two bridges in Derry twice in the last year. Once I was wrecked for days, and that was only about five or six miles. Let's face it, I was grossly unfit with emphasis on the word gross. Now we had the challenge of ten full miles, and Irish ones at that! I think everyone felt it was longer than ten – but perhaps that is because lots of it was uphill from the lake.

Anyhow, when the buses spilled out at the lakeside and the magnificent scenery hove into view, I was flabbergasted to find I was last off apart from Cairán who minded the tail end. Everyone, having polished off, their packed lunch, headed up the road for home. I ate mine on the hoof, so to speak, then started off steadily, with the light rain trying to cool my initial enthusiasm. The weather improved the whole way and by the end it was a beautiful evening with the towering grandeur of Croagh Patrick on the horizon and the lengthening shadows accentuating the beauty of the countryside. I knew if I stopped I would seize up – so I kept going. Two other reasons made me put one foot in front of the other. Number one, I had been sponsored by staff and patients and I knew that, come Monday morning, I would be challenged – "Did you do it?" I knew I could not lie. And then there was Tom McGinley. How on earth could I face him at the end if I gave up and had to be picked up by the bus, or more humiliating, carried home on a stretcher!

Well, a little angel came to my rescue – sent by the Almighty to keep me going - and that was Alina. And she did keep me going. She would walk at my pace when all her friends had disappeared on ahead. She would keep informing me that there was only one more hill when I knew there were hundreds! She kept saying there was only one more corner, when it was obvious there were dozens. Then, when the going got really tough, and I couldn't feel my feet anymore, she used that well known Derry phrase, "Come on, Dr Munro, it's wee buns!!" I now know what this really means, "Look mate, this is real easy and if you can't do it you're a wuss and past it!"

As we struggled up the main street of Louisbourg to the hotel, I said, "Look here, Alina we've just got to jog the last thirty yards, after all the cameras will be out, the tape will be across the road and hundreds will be there to clap us home?" So we did, summoning that last ounce of energy, we jogged those last yards. And do you know what? There was nobody there. Yes! – not a soul! They'd all finished long ago and were in the pubs scattered around the main street slaking their thirst after the rigours of the walk and were not the least bit interested in the tail-enders. Despite this sudden 'downer', and lack of fame at the end, we joined them and I bought my brave Alina a well earned drink. She was the one who got me to the end when it really mattered. I won't forget her every time I'm offered a "wee bun"!

Chapter Thirteen

The Hospice Gardens

'The kiss of the sun for pardon
The song of the bird for mirth
One is nearer to God in a garden
Than anywhere else on earth'   Anon

The advantage of building a hospice on a greenfield site is the opportunity it presents to develop beautiful gardens. Mid-Ulster Gardens were employed to landscape and plant the original gardens. A few years after, the Rotary Club of Londonderry dedicated a *Garden of Tranquillity* in May 1995, on the land above the hospice.

Then, in spring 1996, some employees and 'retirees' from Du Pont were doing their annual tidy-up of the gardens at the hospice. During this Dr McGinley expressed his concerns about the condition of a piece of waste ground opposite the kitchen car park. This ground was steeply sloping and had been used as a dump for debris accumulated during construction. It was now overgrown with weeds and brambles. This area measured about 100m x 50m and was roughly triangular in shape. The men approached their ex-employer with a proposal to clean up, landscape and provide a place of serenity for patients, relatives and staff away from the cares of everyday life. Du Pont supported the project enthusiastically and, with this help, the team of 'retirees' built 60 metres of drystone wall, constructed a pond, patio and a stream. It was completed in 1998.

It was to become called the *Garden of Serenity*. So creative and beautiful was their work that it is entered for the *Unigate Age Concern Award* and won! It was in the category of 'Action for Caring Support'. The award was presented by David Jacobs at a ceremony held in the Guildhall in London in 1997. A few years afterwards they won a further award – the *NICVA Award for Voluntary Work*.

Since 1998, this eager group of retired workers continue to coordinate and execute projects around the hospice. They have built a brick and marble 'welcome' sign, constructed a concrete access path from the new to the older gardens, built new composting facilities and installed new guttering on the conservatory. They also have done general painting. All this was completed with the help of management and trainees from Maydown and Springtown training centres.

During 2002, a workshop/garage facility was built entirely from voluntary donations and offers of free labour. A ride-on lawnmower was funded by local business and individuals. Up to the present time, these men continue to look after the gardens and general day to day maintenance and acknowledge that, without the generous support of Du Pont and other local companies, this work would not have been possible.

Such is the design of the hospice, patients can view the gardens almost everywhere they look. When the weather is fine there is a walk, now completed, right round the extensive gardens.

Along with the Du Pont 'boys', Charlie McCallion assists in the gardens when he can extricate himself from other duties or when he is not driving the hospice minibus.

Barney, Hugh and Danny make up the Dupont Task-Force.
(From left) Barney Gillespie, Neil Hughes, Hugh McLaughlin,
Danny Gorman, Sam Watson (patient), and Rev. Davey.

Hugh McLaughlin

Hugh McLaughlin undertaking some of the back-breaking work.

Danny Gorman keeping a straight eye on the lawn. In 1997, Danny was named Pensioner of the Year by Age Concern, and he is still here! His services in maintenance work are invaluable to the hospice.

The Garden of Serenity

Traditional stone wall with a blaze of tulips in the 'Garden of Serenity'.

Harmony of form in the 'Garden of Serenity'.

The 'Garden of Serenity' in full bloom.

A cascade of bush and flower at the back of the 'Garden of Serenity'.

The Four Seasons
Spring Season – God's renewal of life

Springtime erupts under the trees at the front of the hospice.

Daffodils in spring outside the patient rooms.

Spring in the 'Garden of Tranquillity'.

Peace and quiet in the 'Garden of Tranquillity'.

Harmony of pond, leaf and ducks!

Picturesque scene in the warmth of the summer sun. A granite pillar marking an earth lay-line guarded by a little turf donkey.

Autumn Season – Nature beautiful even in death

The fallen leaf offers sustenance for next spring.

'Garden of Tranquillity' in autumn.

Winter Season – The cold beauty of nature in hibernation

View from the hospice in winter.

The hospice tucked under a clean white blanket.

The beauty of a frozen world surrounds the hospice.

Chapter Fourteen

Dispatches from the Heart

(Extracts from a biography of Tom McGinley KSG, written by Deirdre and the family. This was presented to him at Christmas 2002)

Tom and I were married in 1963. He always showed a great empathy for people dying from cancer. In 1965 he was particularly upset by his inability to sufficiently help a young man dying from cancer. He made up his mind to broaden his knowledge of terminal care, especially pain control. To do this he decided to take sessions in anaesthetics because they were the only experts in pain relief. He reached the conclusion that unless he had a specialist qualification in this field he could not come from a position of strength among his colleagues. He realised it would take many years. Once this task was achieved, armed with this new knowledge, he decided to visit some hospices in England. And so the concept of a hospice here in the North-West began. To this day I wonder did he really realise the magnitude of what he was taking on, but the seed had been sewn – he had a dream and he was determined to fulfil it. All these hospice visits and courses were undertaken at his own expense and during holiday times from his work as a GP. However, he did make sure his family also benefited by leaving aside enough time for us all to have annual holidays in Spain or Donegal.

Tom developed a flu-like illness in autumn 1966. His temperature kept rising and resulted in his admission to Altnagelvin Hospital. Subsequently he was transferred for further investigations to the Royal Victoria Hospital. At first a diagnosis could not be confirmed. His weight plummeted. He began wondering whether the doctors were telling him the truth. He thought I was being secretive too. The specialist thought it was acute sarcoidosis but, in order to confirm this, further investigations were required which included a biopsy. He thought he had cancer and subsequently said, "This was the first time I was confronted with my own mortality. I was terrified and extremely angry with God! I thought I was going to die. I thought I wouldn't see my two young kids grow up."* He went on, "I just couldn't wait for the night nurse to come round and give me Mandrax, which was a very strong sleeping tablet at that time. It had immediate effect."

Tom's mother was a deeply religious woman. She had a great devotion to prayer. She wrote to Tom in hospital in Belfast and said that she had started a novena to Our Lady of the Immaculate Conception. Tom himself had also started the same novena. His mother went on to say that he would begin to improve on 8th December, which was the feast day of the Immaculate Conception. "On that very day," said Tom, "my temperature dropped for the first time in months. I could hardly believe the nurse when she took it and said it was normal." God obviously had something very important that He wanted Tom to complete in his lifetime.

It took a long time for Tom to recover. He began attending Andy McClea's keep-fit gym in Lawrence Hill. Andy recalls that he was then at an extremely low ebb. Andy added, "Exercise became an obsession with him. Indeed he held the record for sit-ups which has never been beaten!" Through the 1970s he first took to squash, then jogging and finally running. During the early 1980s, marathon running became a craze. He ran his first marathon in 1982 in the Foyle Festival. Subsequently Tom ran marathons in Dublin, Belfast, London (several times) and in his birth place of New York. During all these, he managed to raise large sums through sponsorship.

Tom running into Guildhall Square in Derry at the end of the Foyle Festival Marathon. This was his first marathon. (1982)

* Ciarán and Aisling. Rónán and Sinéad had not yet been born.

Tom at the finish of his first London marathon (1985). His time was 3hrs and 7 minutes, which was his best ever. He never did achieve his goal of under 3 hrs.

Once the site had been found, the new Foyle Bridge was adopted as the logo for the hospice. The bridge evoked for him the concept of the journey between life and death. It was also a symbol of the removal of the division that seemed to exist between the Waterside and Cityside in Derry. This hospice was to be for all sections of the community regardless of creed or politics.

When the land had been bought, and the spirit of the new hospice permeated the Derry population as well as Strabane and Inishowen, there was a great urge to raise funds. Very soon, all that was being talked about was this new hospice that was going to make such a difference to terminally ill patients and their relatives. There was soon nothing the community would, nor could, not do to help spur things on. Fundraising took many forms. Indeed, anything in any shape or form that would help raise money was undertaken.

My heart went out to all those who contributed to the success of the hospice.

I hope that the community as a whole know how much their efforts at fundraising are so much appreciated, however small they think their input is. Nothing is too small – it is all cumulative. I find it impossible to mention all the people and groups who have made Tom's dream possible and I hope I am forgiven for that, but heartfelt thanks goes out to all of them. I have never seen a project develop with such momentum in all my life, and on and on it goes.

Tom's dream became a reality in June 1991 with the official opening of the Inpatient Unit. God surely smiled on us that day because it was one of the very few warm sunny days that year. It was as though He was saying: 'Well done my true and faithful servant.' It was an unforgettable day attended by many local

Deirdre with Tom at the 'People of the Year Award'.

and other dignitaries, and the memories will stay in our hearts forever. Tom has been the recipient of many awards for all his good work.

Of particular significance to him was receiving the inaugural 'Graduate of the Year Award' from his university in Galway. We were all so pleased that he had the recognition he so well deserved. He accepted the awards, but with great humility, because he has always felt that they really belong to the community who have worked so very hard to make his dream a reality.

The 10th Anniversary of the Opening of the Hospice was celebrated in the White Horse Inn in June 2001. It was another outstanding occasion for Tom as well as for everyone present. It was a memorable and emotional evening.

Deirdre and Tom cutting the cake at the 10th anniversary of the opening of the Foyle Hospice Inpatient Unit.

In February 2002, he received a Papal Knighthood of the Equestrian Order of St Gregory the Great, and that too was a wondrous occasion, participated in by all our family and friends in St Eugene's Cathedral. I think he is in awe at being recognised by His Holiness Pope John Paul for all his work and we, as his family, continue to feel so very proud of him. And yet his work for the hospice continues and will do until the day he dies. Of that I am sure.

It is indeed amazing to see what Tom has achieved in such a short time, especially as so many people thought he was mad even to consider taking on something of this magnitude and they really didn't think he would achieve it. But, guess what, I knew he would and so did he. The fact that he has been able to help so many people to have a pain-free, dignified death has given him the greatest satisfaction. It is something to which we are all entitled and it took this amazing husband of mine to make that dream come true for so many.

Tom's biography, compiled by Deirdre and the family was presented to him at Christmas 2002. On 2nd January, 2003, Tom and Deirdre celebrated their 40th Wedding Anniversary (Ruby). Father Graham celebrated Mass at Thornhill and his friends Bishop Daly and Bishop Mehaffey were present. Deirdre had developed breast cancer some nine years previously but had continued to work at her profession, as a pharmacist, until a few weeks before her death. Once Deirdre reached that important milestone of the Ruby Anniversary, she decided that she would forgo any further active treatment for her cancer. She indicated her wish to be nursed at home. Tom arranged to take time off work to help the family with her care. Her wholehearted support for Tom was well known. Her courage towards the end of her own life is not so well known. Tom says that she achieved a serenity that was deeply spiritual, at peace with God and at peace with the world. On the night before she died she thanked Tom and said she thought the end was near. She died peacefully in the early hours of 7th June, 2003.

Tom decided to donate a gazebo in the grounds of the hospice, in memory of Deirdre, so that patients and staff could enjoy a little privacy and meditation. This was completed for the first anniversary of her death on 7th June, 2004 when Mass was celebrated by Bishop Daly in the Day Centre. He had been present at their marriage on 2nd January, 1963.

Cutting the cake at the 40th anniversary, six months before Deirdre died.

Patients and staff outside the gazebo.

*Aisling McGinley, Elaine Duffy (Deirdre's sister),
Sinéad McGinley, Ursula Nugent (Deirdre's sister).*

My personal tribute to a wonderful husband

There is nothing in this world that I could buy, or nothing that I could do for Tom, to repay the care, encouragement and undying love that he has given me, especially over the last eight years in my own battle with cancer and two recurrences. He has been alongside me every step of the way, while still tending to so many others suffering the same disease as me. To say that he has gone that extra mile with me is an understatement. I would not be writing this today except for those qualities which God instilled in him and which he has put to such wonderful use, often in the face of adversity. So many people thought he was crazy when he first started to fundraise for a hospice in the north-west. Well, he has proved that he isn't so crazy after all.

Thank you Tom, I cannot believe what a fortunate woman I am to have such a remarkable and compassionate husband.

God is surely on my side too.

With all my love forever

Deirdre

(This tribute was part of Tom's biography written by Deirdre and the family)

Picture Gallery

Report in the press which kick-started Dr McGinley to begin raising money.

Willie 'Balbo' Carson, well-known photographer, seen here (left) at the end of the Foyle Female Five in 1983. He took many photographs for the hospice and was extremely supportive of the work.

The Mayor, Councillor Len Green, welcomes William Doherty (on left) and Donal Dunne (second right) on the completion of their sponsored run from Dublin to Derry in aid of Foyle Hospice. Included are Eugene Dunne, transport manger for the run, and Dr Tom, who accompanied the runners over the last few miles. (May 1984)

Dr McGinley, Chairman of Foyle Hospice, together with Dr Munro, Vice-Chairman, accepting a cheque from the Honourable the Irish Society who were very supportive of the project in the early days. (1984)

A large cheque being presented to Dr Tom McGinley. This money was the proceeds of an exhibition and sale of artworks held in the Orchard Gallery during December 1984. It was organised by Ken McGilloway, who became one of the Trustees of the hospice. Mr Harvey FRCS is to the left with Mayor John Tierney on the right. In the middle is Willie Doherty, the curator of the Orchard Gallery.

Sponsored bike ride. Dr Keith with his own children and staff from Clarendon Medical, his own practice. (1985)

A generous cheque presented by All Saints Clooney Youth Club in March 1985.

Official launch of the Homecare Programme in December 1985. Eighty GPs attended at 9 Crawford Square. (Left) Dr Peter Fallon (deceased), Angela McIntyre, Dr Tom, Rosemary Houston, Dr Seán O'Sullivan from Rathmullan (deceased), Hannah Walsh.

Father Joe Carolan with Jackie Deeney presenting a cheque to Dr Tom. Father Joe died in the hospice on 28th August, 1999. (September 1987)

Dr Tom receiving cheques totalling £2000 from Derry Telephone Exchange staff, Winnie Brown and Angelo Delpinto. The pair won the money for charity in the British Telecom Northern Ireland Golden Heart Awards in recognition of their past fundraising efforts. Winnie came second in the individual category, and presented her £500 to the hospice while Angelo presented £1500, the top group prize won by local operators and engineers. Included (from left) Rita Quinn, Seamus McGeehan, Terry Casey and Anne Ferry. BT employees installed the original telephone system in the hospice voluntarily. They continued to help in various ways over the years.

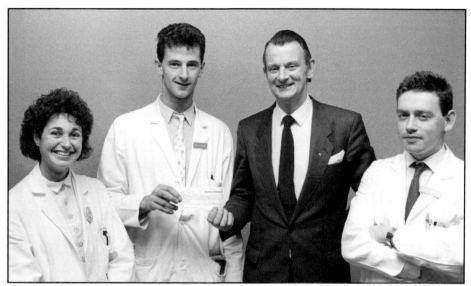

Dr Lee Casey presents a cheque to Dr McGinley in 1987. This money was collected from organised functions at Altnagelvin Hospital. Also present are Dr Muriel Fitzsimmons and Dr Joe McEvoy.

The Co-Leck Inter-denominational Group. Their fundraising venture raised major sums for the hospice. (Left) Hannah, Rev. Bell (Presbyterian), Father Harkin (Catholic), Rev. Tilson (Church of Ireland), Rosemary and Dr Tom. Father Harkin is deceased.

Dr John Hart, a General Practitioner, presenting a cheque in the late 1980s. He died in the hospice on 17th June, 1997. Hannah was a district nurse in his practice prior to becoming a homecare nurse for the hospice.

Pictured are some of the participants in the 1988 annual sponsored walk, who raised over £700 for hospice funds. Presenting the proceeds to Dr Tom is the Very Rev. Dean Cecil Orr. (Front left) Mrs Collette Dolan, Ella Hegarty, Catherine McGilloway, St Columba's Girls P.S., Tracey Dunne, Aidan McLean, and Mrs June Peoples, Lisnagelvin P.S. (Back left) Martin Bradley, Fintan Bradley, Dennis Villa, Alistair Kinkaid, Foyle Hospice and John Coyle.

Rev. Wesley Blair, Strabane, presents a cheque to Dr Tom. Jackie Blair, his wife, is also present together with Angela and Hannah (left). This money came from his sponsored cycle from Mizen Head to Malin head. (April 1991)

At the awards ceremony in the Grand Hotel, Malahide, for 'Donegal Person of the Year'. (March 1992) Tom, with his long-time partners and friends, Dr Vincent Cavanagh (left) and Dr Peter Fallon (right)

Dr Marcus McGrenra from Ardara in Donegal was a long-time friend of Dr Tom's. They boarded together in St Eunan's College Secondary College in Letterkenny. They then spent six years together in digs while studying medicine in Galway. After qualification they both worked in Portiuncula Hospital in Ballinasloe, Co Galway. Tom came to Derry and Marcus went to Bolton. He was a GP and part-time anaesthetist – just like Tom. He later developed cancer and spent many weeks of respite care in Foyle Hospice. His last period of respite was during August 1999. He subsequently died in Bolton. Hospice staff used to torture him for juicy bits of scandal about Tom's life at university!

'People of the Year Award' 1999, where Tom and Brian Friel received awards. Included are Church of Ireland Archbishop Donald and Mrs Caird, Mrs Friel and Bishop James Mehaffey with his wife Thelma.

Emma Robinson and Clare McLaughlin with Her Grace the Duchess of Norfolk a short time after the official opening of the hospice. Mayor Mary Bradley and Dr McGinley are also present. Nicholas Brolly (5), whose father died of cancer in 1992, is at the front.

Opening of the Garden of Tranquillity. Graham Hunter cuts the ribbon on behalf of the Rotary Club, flanked by Rosemary and Dr Tom. (May 1995)

Forum on Palliative Care, 21st February, 1990 held at Magee University. (From left) Jean Harper, Matron of Beaconsfield Marie Curie Home, Dr Osmond Morris, Medical Director of Newry Hospice, Dr Tom; Peter Quigley, Administrative Director of the Northern Ireland Hospice, and Rita Beattie, Nursing Director of the Northern Ireland Hospice.

Dr Tom McGinley pictured at a seminar on "The Child with Cancer" held at the White Horse Inn, Campsie. Included (from left) Most Rev. Dr Edward Daly, Ms Dorothy Judd, Paediatric Psychotherapist, Dr Finn Breathnach, Consultant Paediatric Oncologist, Dr Mary Ryan, Consultant Haematologist at Altnagelvin Hospital. (Back from left), Teresa McSwiney, Aisling McGinley, Rosemary Peoples and Dr Morris Browne, Medical Advisor, Western Area Board. (8th March, 1996)

The launch of a CD/Tape called 'Across the Bridge', a fundraising initiative for Foyle Hospice. Included are Dominic Kirwan, Bishop Daly, Willie Loughlin, Frances Campbell, Michael Kielty, Rónán Doherty and Nancy Moran. (November 1996)

Retirement function for Gretta Linehan and Theresa McSwiney. Hannah and Rosemary are still going strong!

Car Draw in Foyleside in 2000. Rosemary, David Ayton (Belfast Telegraph), Tom, Des Farrell,(Manager of Foyleside) and Ciarán. The car was donated anonymously by a reader of the Belfast Telegraph who had won it in one of their competitions.

Winner of the Millennium Draw. Pat Cowley and his daughter look happy, if surprised, at their good fortune.

Prize-winners of the Millennium Run/Walk at the Guildhall.
Included are Yvonne Martin and Hannah Healy.

Kathleen Boyle, (hospice volunteer), and Ursula Nugent handing out medals
after the 2001 Female Five Walk.

10th Anniversary Celebrations

Letting off balloons at the front of the hospice. Local schools at the 10th Anniversary of the Opening of the Hospice. (2001)

T'ai Chi in the gardens – easing tension in the quiet of nature. Tenth Anniversary of the Opening (2001)

Relaxing in the sun at a hospice open day.

Irish dancing in the front hall for patients and relatives.

The 10th Anniversary of the Opening of the Inpatient Unit

Some of the Trustees at the 10th Anniversary Ball held in the White Horse Inn, 2001. (From left): Ken McGilloway, Jim Guy, Neil Doherty, Dr Tom, Angela McIntyre, Paddy Kelly, Dr Keith.

Tom with Yvonne Martin and Hannah Healy at the 10th Anniversary Ball.

Tom's Papal Knighthood Investiture – February 2002

John Hume MEP presenting Tom with a cheque for £30,000, part of the 'Gandhi Peace Prize'. Included are Pat Hume and Deirdre. When Tom took time off to care for Deirdre, Pat and John's daughter, Dr Áine Abbott acted as a locum at the hospice and was popular with both patients and staff.

Tom and Deirdre with the family. (From left) Ciáran, Aisling, Sinéad, Rónán

Maureen Hegarty leading the singing of 'The Fields of Athenry' (Tom's favourite song) together with Tom and Aisling. Maureen has been a staunch supporter of the hospice since the early days. "I didn't have much choice because Tom was my GP!" She organized a very successful concert in Greencastle, which boosted hospice funds significantly, and has taken part in many functions held in the Day Centre. Maureen is well-known throughout Ireland for her singing talents and is the local personality regularly requested to draw out the winning tickets at car draws and, at the same time, entertain the crowds. The beautiful performance on the harp, by Declan her son, at the 10th Anniversary Ball (2001), was greatly appreciated.

Dr Keith congratulating Dr Tom.

Dr Tom with Rev. Maurice Bolton.

Charlie McCallion with his friend, 'the Doctor'.

Dr Tom with nursing staff at the function held in the hospice Daycare Centre following the Papal Investiture.

Enjoying the good weather, while it occurred! Betty Kane is seen here with Donna, Dr Anne Donnelly, Patricia and Mary. Betty died in the hospice on 13th November, 2004.Her brother switched on the Christmas lights in 2004.

Tommy Kelly, Staff Nurse.

The four homecare sisters, 2004. (From left) Monica Cunningham, Yvonne Martin, Mary Collins and Hannah Healy. Both Yvonne and Mary have now moved to work for the Donegal Hospice and Rosie Green (see inset) has joined the present homecare team.

Margaret Gallagher presents a cheque for £900 to Dr Tom. This money was in lieu of birthday gifts for her 90th Birthday. Included is her daughter, Carmel McDonald, and Terri Sythes (right). (2005 – see chapter 3)

Eddie Mailey is a volunteer in the Daycare Centre. He helps with the transport of patients and runs quizzes and other entertainments.

Ciarán Dorney, a very keen supporter, holding the Sam Maguire Cup recently won by Tyrone in the GAA football final against Kerry. His teacher, from the Holy Child School in Creggan, had arranged for the cup to visit Ciarán in the hospice, where he is an inpatient. (1st October, 2005)

The gazebo nestling in the hospice gardens facing the River Foyle.

*Hallowe'en party held at the Day Centre. Pictured are
patients, staff and volunteers. (2005)*

Gala Ball

On 29 October, 2005, 200 people gathered at the City Hotel to celebrate 20 years of hospice care in the North-West.

*Tom and Hannah enjoy cutting the cake. Hannah Healy
was the first employee of Foyle Hospice.*

Tom with members of the nursing staff, past and present.

Tom and his three friends from Ardavon House.
(From left) Kathleen, Bernadette, and Dymphna.

Four of the original group who launched Foyle Hospice Appeal in 1985.

Tom enjoys a lighthearted moment with Bishop Ken Goode (left) and his wife Mary, and Bishop James Mehaffey and his wife Thelma.

Staunch fundraisers for Foyle Hospice. (From left) Cathal Curley, Dr Keith, Bernie Mount, Dr Tom and Martin McCrossan.

Tom and Deirdre after Christmas morning Mass at the hospice.

Committee Members and Trustees

The Hospice Family
An ever increasing family circle

The hospice, as well as the people associated with it, is a family.
This special family is one consisting of ever increasing circles.

The FIRST circle, the very heart and centre of the family, is the patient who is a unique individual with a special life. The patient is the very reason for the existence of the hospice and its focus for love and caring.

The SECOND circle consists of family members and those who matter to the patient.

The THIRD circle consists of chaplains, doctors, nursing and ancillary staff. They are all dedicated groups of people who respect the dignity of each individual patient and care for all their needs both medical and spiritual.

The FOURTH circle consists of volunteers.
Their work is invaluable to the running and the success of the hospice.

The FIFTH, and outer, circle is the community, whose wholehearted support embraces the hospice and whose most outstanding quality is their generous nature.